Textbook Rationality

Rationality—and why we should teach it in schools

IVAN PHILLIPS

TEXTBOOK RATIONALITY

Copyright © 2021 Ivan Phillips

Barley Lane Books

PO Box 5613, Buffalo Grove, IL 60089

www.barleylanebooks.com

January 27 2021

First Edition, 2021

Edited by Koka Kliora

ISBNs: 978-1-7365783-0-8 (paperback); 978-1-7365783-1-5 (ebook)
        978-1-7365783-3-9 (hardcover)

10 9 8 7 6 5 4 3 2 1

The Rational Future Institute

The goal of the Rational Future Institute is to create a cultural awareness of the principles of ideal rationality and of the ways we humans predictably deviate from rational thinking.

Find us online:

https://rationalfuture.org

facebook.com/rationalfuture

@rationalfuture

CONTENTS

PREFACE

This book is about the fundamental principles of rational thinking. These are principles that everybody should know, but which our schools do not teach. One can excel in one's academic career, obtain an advanced degree in science, mathematics, or philosophy, and still never have received any formal training in rational thinking. I know this because it happened to me.

I have always had a passion for science and critical thinking. After earning my doctoral degree in theoretical physics from Northwestern University in 1993, I went on to a career in the software industry. Outside of work, I spent considerable time promoting science and critical thinking as a member of local science groups. In 2010, I gave a presentation on rational thinking to an audience of scientists, doctors, business managers, lawyers, engineers, and students. My presentation was well-received. Yet shortly thereafter, I was shocked to discover huge gaps in my understanding. I had not truly understood the meaning of the term rationality, nor had I been aware of its core principles. Apparently, my audience had been none the wiser. I was flummoxed. How could I have made it this far through my career without learning the fundamentals? Moreover, how could I, of all people, have not noticed this sooner?

Despite a graduate-level education in science, I had never received any explicit education in the fundamentals of rationality. This was not a flaw in my personal academic history, but a failure of the academy in general. There are no standard courses on rational thinking in high schools or colleges.

In this book, I aim to provide you with an accessible overview of rational thinking. But I aim to do something arguably more important—I want to give you the big picture on rational thinking. I want to explain why formal rationality has thus far failed to become a social phenomenon. I want to help you imagine a more responsible society, one that treats rational thinking as a serious academic discipline while also respecting human values.

* * *

I thank Leon Phillips, Debra Sancho, Margaret Przybysz, Scott Thompson, Casella Brookins, Evgeny Kolev, Ross Doyle, and Tina Garcia for their feedback on early drafts of this book.

Ivan Phillips

The Rational Future Institute

January 2021

1 INTRODUCTION

1.1 Rationality

Rationality is something we all desire. We aspire to be the rational parent, the rational manager, the rational consumer, the rational voter. Yet what does it actually mean to be a rational person?

Think about this question for a couple of minutes. Later, ask your friends and co-workers this same question, and you are likely to hear a multitude of different answers.

If you are like most people, you will find it difficult to give a definition of rationality in simple terms. Instead, you probably have a fuzzy notion of what rationality means, an idea cloud consisting of things you associate with rational people. You may describe a rational person as logical, scientific, and analytical— all adjectives associated with the most arduous of thinking tasks. You may also describe rational people as calm, collected, even emotionless. I have even heard rationality equated with a cold-blooded, self-centered, and greedy demeanor.

Respectively, these three sets of adjectives make rational thinking sound painful, joyless, and selfish. With associations like these, there is little wonder then that we have a kind of love/hate relationship with rationality. We want the rewards of rationality, but we recoil from the notion that we ought to behave like robots.

The good news is that this dissonance is misplaced. Rationality has nothing to do with a selfish or unemotional demeanor. Simply put, thinking rationally means making proper inferences. A rational person knows how to reason to conclusions that are most likely to be true.

1.2 Why Rationality?

Democratic civilization rests on the premise of an educated and wise electorate. No matter what democratic political values we hold, if our citizens cannot distinguish reality from fiction, the resulting policy will lead us to social, economic, environmental, and military ruin.

The world is on the brink of a rationality catastrophe. Human knowledge is growing at an exponential rate. Knowledge is a good thing, of course, but the sphere of human knowledge is expanding beyond the ability of individual human minds to grasp it all. Thanks to the Internet, we now have access to more information than at any previous time in human history, yet making sense of that information is increasingly more difficult. To make matters worse, we are drowning in digital misinformation—both deliberate and unintended—and the challenge of extracting understanding from information is greater than ever.

Introduction

Rationality is the cure for this problem. Rationality is the technical ability to make sense out of information, and while our untrained minds sometimes possess enough rationality to make sense out of our personal lives, our rational instincts fall far short of what we need to stave off disaster in the long run.

Imagine instead a world populated by rational versions of ourselves. In such a world, we would not be flawless thinking machines, but we would at least know how we *ought* to think and be aware of all the ways we were likely to stray from proper reasoning. People would make rational judgments based on available evidence, and withhold their judgment when facts were scarce and insufficient. Citizens could read about scientific and medical research, competently see through media hype, and know when and how to trust in experts and technology to fill in the gaps. The inhabitants of this more rational world would understand how to separate information from misinformation, and how to apply a new generation of technologies to the problem of information overload. Of course, such a rational world would still have plenty of disagreements about policy and value, but they would at least agree on the facts and truths underlying our decisions.

Now, imagine that this fantastic world is just a generation away. This is the promise of rationality education. It could save civilization.

What I find most inspiring is that rationality education is simple, feasible, and obvious in hindsight. Thanks to research programs in the 20th century, experts have already acquired the fundamentals of rational thinking. All we need to do is teach that knowledge and allow it to seep into the public consciousness.

1.3   The Intended Audience for This Book

This book is a primer on rational thinking. It is also a manifesto for changes to our culture and educational system.

The book is intended for anyone looking for a gentle introduction to rational thinking. I believe this book will appeal most to people who already have a passion for the truth and for careful thinking.

Educators are among the most passionate advocates for clear thinking. Educators have been trying to teach critical thinking for decades, and there is both an overlap and a synergy between critical thinking and rational thinking. I will argue that rational thinking may be the best way to teach students how to think critically. This is not a textbook, though it could serve as reading material for a beginner's course on rationality. I hope that this work will serve as inspiration for educators and textbook authors who are better qualified to create instructional materials.

In creating this primer on rational thinking, my objective has been to give readers a simple organizing principle, a reference point from which rational thinking topics make sense. I hope that experts in rationality and philosophy will not only forgive my oversimplifications but be inspired to write their own works for students.

1.4   The Myth of Human Rationality

Aristotle defined humans as the rational animal, distinguishing us from all the other species on Earth by our ability to reason. The fact that we can infer the equations that govern the operation of the universe and use those formulas to fly a spacecraft through a gap in the rings of Saturn is surely testament to our rationality. Indeed, the crown jewels of our civilization—science, medicine, mathematics, art, literature, architecture, and our economic systems—could only have been engineered using our rationality. Though our rationality is real, the stories we tell ourselves about rationality are more like fairy tales.

Rationality is about updating our beliefs based on evidence in such a way that we can make better predictions about the future. Rationality converts information into knowledge. Through experience and dedication, through our cultural institutions, we have amassed great stores of knowledge. The mythology of reason enters when we construct a narrative about how we reached our conclusions.

We explain our conclusions in terms of arguments. Arguments are like directions to a destination. By giving an argument, we are explaining to others how they too might navigate their way to the same conclusion. However, in giving an argument, we are rarely describing our own journey to our conclusion.

We naturally think of reason as proceeding in a forward direction—evidence and argument precede a conclusion. Yet most of the time, we reason in reverse. Many of our beliefs emerge through trial and error, instinct, or indoctrination. Later, when asked to explain why we hold our beliefs, we reverse-engineer a suitable argument as an excuse or rationalization for why we ended up where we did. Our conclusion comes first, and arguments are invented later.

In principle, there is nothing wrong with reasoning in reverse. A good argument is not only a good excuse to hold a conclusion, but also a good map for future thinkers to reach that same conclusion. However, multiple things tend to go wrong when we reason in reverse. First, our reverse-engineering is often faulty and incomplete. For most conclusions, there are multiple arguments, *pro* and *con*. Our habit is to satisfy ourselves with the first *pro* argument we can find while ignoring any *con* arguments. Second, we pay little attention to the reversed nature of our reasoning. Instead of telling the true story of how we initially stumbled across the right conclusion, we prefer the fiction that we used tight, logical arguments from the start. This makes us feel more rational and impartial than we truly are.

The myth, then, is that we reason forward, using clear rules and arguments. The truth is that we are highly inconsistent and are more fixated on defending our initial conclusions than in finding the truth.

1.5 Critical Thinking

Overcoming the flaws in our reasoning requires critical thinking. The idea is simple. If our initial beliefs and the arguments we use to support them are sometimes arbitrary, biased, and one-sided, then we can become more rational by being more critical and systematic. Where did our belief originate? Are our arguments consistent? Does the evidence support them? Are there equally powerful arguments against our belief?

Critical thinking techniques are usually presented as a collection of corrective procedures, such as carefully evaluating the sources of evidence, thoroughly exploring all the relevant arguments, and making explicit assumptions.

Critical thinking is a mature discipline. Research demonstrates that critical thinking is an effective, learnable skill.[1] There are numerous books on the subject, and most educators attempt to teach their students critical thinking skills at some level. A few high schools and colleges even teach critical thinking as a dedicated course.

---

[1] Abrami PC, Bernard RM, Borokhovski E, Waddington DI, Wade CA, Persson T. *Strategies for Teaching Students to Think Critically: A Meta-Analysis.* Review of Educational Research. 2015;85(2):275-314.

https://doi.org/10.3102/0034654314551063.

There is one important topic that is neglected by traditional critical thinking education: ideal rationality. Ideal rationality is the method by which an ideal rational mind would move from evidence to conclusion. You can think of ideal reasoning as the algorithm we would program into a computer to make it reason as accurately as possible.

1.6   Ideal Rationality

Many people take critical thinking and rationality to be synonymous. In this traditional view, the ideal rational mind is a mind not dissimilar to our own, but for the difference that it thinks critically to a maximal degree. This view makes some sense because critical thinking is the route from intuitive human thinking to something more rational.

The alternative view—the view to which I cleave—distinguishes between critical thinking and rationality. We can imagine machines that reason so perfectly that they do not require critical thinking to correct their reasoning. Such ideal reasoning machines, even hypothetical ones, would serve as a sort of gold standard against which human judgments could be compared. If we can determine how an ideal reasoning system would think, we can begin to ask questions such as, "Would the ideal reasoner concur with my judgment?" or "Would an ideal reasoner share this belief with me?" Having a standard of ideal reason would also put critical thinking into perspective. In this view, critical thinking would be the checklist of corrections we go through to correct human thinking and return it to the path of the hypothetical ideal reasoner.

If the methods used by the ideal mind were mysterious or infinitely complex, then the traditional and alternative views of ideal rationality would be virtually indistinguishable. With no way to define the ideal except by maximal critical thinking, critical and rational thinking would have the same meaning. However, there is a strong candidate for the gold standard of rational judgment: Bayesian inference.

Bayes' theorem is a formula in probability theory that tells us how we ought to update our beliefs in response to new evidence. This is a beautiful and powerful result. We humans are constantly updating our beliefs based on what we see and what we read, but instead of using a formula, we use our intuition. We make a gut judgment about how much each piece of evidence should affect our beliefs, or whether to accept the evidence at all. What Bayes' theorem tells us is that there is an ideal way to update our beliefs that emerges from the logic of probability.

Since ideal rationality can be defined in mathematical terms, critical thinking and rationality have distinct meanings. For humans, rationality is only attainable through critical thinking, whereas an ideally rational mind would have no need for critical thinking because it would reason correctly the first time and have no need for correction.

One of the theses of this book is that ideal rationality is a useful concept for teaching and understanding critical thinking. There are valid criticisms of this thesis, and I will address them later in this chapter. First, I will explain why ideal rationality is useful for critical thinking.

Traditionally, critical thinking is taught as a long list of countermeasures we can employ to overcome our irrationality. Though the countermeasures are effective, I always found it difficult to mentally compress the list into a few simple principles. To me, this lack of a simple recipe for correct thinking is a weakness of the traditional approach.

While Bayesian inference is a candidate for ideal reasoning, it is rarely taught as such. Bayesian inference can be found in most textbooks on probability and statistics, and some books on critical thinking will employ Bayesian methods as one problem-solving tool among many. Indeed, it is difficult to employ the Bayesian formulas everywhere, and so its direct mathematical utility is limited. However, even when Bayes' theorem is not used to calculate a number, it provides a useful map of how we ought to think. Many forms of irrational thinking can be framed as violations of Bayesian inference.

The Bayesian approach gives us a much-needed big picture, helping us see the ingredients we need to reach rational conclusions and build our intuitions for how the process of rational thinking is supposed to work.

1.7 Soft Skill Versus Technical Discipline

The pervading ethos in contemporary society is that rationality is a talent or personality trait. In truth, rationality is a teachable, technical skill. At least, it ought to be.

In contemporary society, rationality is not yet taught as a technical proficiency. There is no standard educational course on rational thinking, no rationality section at your local bookstore, and no set of standard tests or credentials. Nonetheless, we employ rational thinking skills in our daily lives, if unreliably. How do we manage to be rational without having been formally trained?

Societies have always treated rationality as a soft skill. Soft skills are the type of expertise you pick up outside of a classroom, and they rely heavily on subconscious intuition. One can possess a soft skill without a conscious understanding of the steps required to perform the skill. A soft skill can be physical, such as walking or playing tennis, or it can be intellectual, such as evaluating a product purchase or the strength of a sports team.

The advantage of soft skills is that we can often apply them with hardly a conscious thought. For example, when we speak to people, we do not need to think about grammar or vocabulary. Though we may have conscious awareness of what we wish to say, the words we use to express our thoughts often pour forth without much conscious attention. Indeed, speaking is so effortless for many of us that we do it for fun.

Before the advent of formal education, people were successfully speaking to each other, trading, and making rational judgments. People successfully acquired these skills through practice and experience, but without any formal training in grammar, economics, accounting, or probability theory.

The disadvantage of soft skills is that they operate like black boxes. Since we typically lack conscious awareness of how our soft skills work, we tend to treat them like natural talents or mysterious gifts. We speak of the "gifted genius," the friend with the "gift of gab," and "born leaders." Because soft skills are invisible, it is difficult to diagnose their failure when they let us down. Often, we merely shrug and say, "To err is human" or "I lack the talent for that."

History teaches us that transforming a soft skill into a technical or professional discipline can result in an immense leap forward for a civilization. Many of these transformations have marked key inflection points in human progress. Language, agriculture, trade, medicine, construction, food preparation, and psychology were once the exclusive province of intuition and gut instinct. Today, these fields are technical disciplines demanding college degrees or professional qualifications. Formalization and professionalization have made the products and practices of each of these fields better and more reliable. Today, we live in greater comfort and safety than ever before because of the advancement of these soft skills into technical or professional disciplines.

Professionalization has also made disciplines more accessible in that there is a well-defined educational path to expertise. Professional expertise is more consistent and shared across more experts. For instance, becoming a physician is a matter of enrolling in the relevant educational programs and persistence with internship and practical work. Of course, passion and general intelligence can increase the chances of success, but most of the work is a matter of understanding and executing technical skills. Contrast this with the era of soft skills, where a trainee would apprentice with a local, isolated expert, learning without the aid of written materials.

Of all the soft skills our civilization has transformed into technical fields, rational thinking is the most neglected. As a dedicated course, rationality is almost totally absent from the standard high school and college curriculum, and even professional scientists and mathematicians have likely received no explicit training in ideal rational thinking. However, experts in rationality and decision making do exist. These specialists usually come from one of three fields: cognitive psychology, behavioral economics, and artificial intelligence. Together, these experts can tell us what ideal reasoning looks like, how human reasoning deviates from the ideal, and what we can do to get back on course. To revolutionize the way our culture thinks about reasoning, all we need to do is transfer this existing knowledge to the general population in a way that helps people reason more effectively.

1.8   Epistemic and Instrumental Rationality

Imagine an ideal reasoning machine that tabulates every piece of evidence it observes and correctly reasons forward from that evidence to the conclusions that are most likely to be true. When more than one conclusion is plausible, the machine ranks each conclusion by probability, keeping track of its uncertainty. Such a machine could be used to compute which of several competing scientific theories would most likely be true. It could also be used to calculate the probabilities of future events, such as elections, crop yields, or natural disasters.

This hypothetical ideal reasoning machine acts like a bookmaker, systematically estimating the odds that each possibility is true. As I have defined it, the machine is disinterested in anything but the likely truth of its theories. Indeed, the sole objective of such a machine is perfectly justified knowledge of the world. There is no guarantee that our reasoning machine would always win every bet about future events, but it would make the best possible bets given the available information. The kind of rationality practiced by our machine is known as *epistemic rationality*. An epistemically rational entity is one whose beliefs about the world are as accurate as possible.

While curiosity is admirable, a pathological quest for knowledge for knowledge's sake is rather alien to us. Though we place some intrinsic value on knowledge, we primarily seek knowledge as a means to some end. For us, knowledge is power because understanding our world enables us to meet our goals and take actions that effectively satisfy our preferences. We rely on epistemic rationality to inform our decisions, but our goal is to win at the game of life. When we act in a fashion that is a suitable to our ends, we are said to be exhibiting *instrumental rationality*. In crude terms, epistemic rationality is about knowing what is true, while instrumental rationality is about using that knowledge to satisfy our values.

Much of the literature on rationality is classified into either epistemic or instrumental rationality. Articles about epistemic rationality help us assess statistical evidence and better judge the likely outcomes of our actions. Articles about instrumental rationality often read like self-help material, trying to answer questions like, "How can we make better use of our time and money to get more out of life?" or "How can we use psychology and philosophy to live a life that is happier and more consistent with our values?"

Good instrumental rationality requires that we know what we value, but it is not always easy to figure out what we want out of life. Our values and preferences change as we grow older and gain new and varied experiences. Our values may even change in response to how a question is framed. As it turns out, optimally satisfying preferences is difficult even when we know what is true about the world.

For several reasons, I have chosen to focus this book on epistemic rationality. Epistemic rationality is a prerequisite for instrumental rationality, and good epistemic rationality is a foundation for future instrumental thinking. Moreover, epistemic rationality is less subjective and more straightforward than instrumental rationality.

1.9 Facts and Values

Facts are valuable. We use rationality to figure out how the world works and how to create the best life we can for ourselves and those we love. Consider the following line of reasoning:

1. Seatbelts prevent death and severe injuries in the event of a car crash.

2. There are thousands of car crashes each year.

3. Widespread adoption of seatbelt use will save thousands of lives every year.

4. To save lives and reduce overall suffering, everyone ought to wear a seatbelt while driving or riding in a car.

This whole chain of reasoning seems to make sense. Statement 3 follows from statements 1 and 2. To the uninitiated, statement 4 seems like it might follow automatically from the previous statements. However, there is an important difference between the first three statements and the fourth. Whereas the first three statements state facts about what seatbelts will do, the fourth statement is making a value judgment, telling us what we ought to do with that information. Those who feel that we should accept a minor inconvenience to save lives may see the two statements as saying the same thing. However, the fourth statement only follows from the third when that connection is made explicit. Let's insert a fifth statement which will connect 3 and 4:

Introduction

1. Seatbelts prevent death and severe injuries in the event of a car crash.

2. There are thousands of car crashes each year.

3. Widespread adoption of seatbelt use will save thousands of lives every
    year.

    a. We ought to accept minor inconveniences to save lives.

4. To save lives and reduce overall suffering, everyone ought to wear a
    seatbelt while driving or riding in a car.

With the addition of 3a, the chain of reasoning is complete, and 4 follows from
the previous statements. Here is the interesting part: The additional statement
that we inserted to connect the fact with the value judgment is itself a statement
of value. It turns out that we can never derive an "ought" statement from
statements of fact without inserting another "ought" statement earlier in the chain
of reason. It follows that no collection of purely descriptive facts can justify a value
judgment on their own. The Scottish philosopher David Hume is credited with
first enunciating this is-ought distinction—you cannot get an *ought* from an *is*.

Rationality has its limitations. We can use reason to connect descriptive facts to
each other. We can use reason to show that our values and goals cohere with each
other and with descriptive facts. However, we cannot use reason to manufacture
a value from nothing but descriptive facts.

If values are not determined by descriptive facts, what does determine them?
This is a question for philosophers, but I shall take values to be defined by what

we care about. What we care about changes from moment to moment, but after careful consideration, we usually reach a sort of reflective equilibrium. Averaging over our mood swings and accounting for competing values, we can usually say what matters to us most.

Making a distinction between facts and values is vital to rational thinking. If we cannot isolate our values from facts, we can blind ourselves to reality and ultimately frustrate the very values and goals we are trying to protect. When we focus exclusively on the facts, we can reach a more accurate understanding of the world. With this understanding achieved, we can bring our values back into the picture and find the best way to satisfy our objectives.

1.10   Rational, Irrational, and Nonrational

Before we dive into an explanation of rationality itself, we must dispel the common myth that rationality entails a spartan, robotlike demeanor.

It is a common misconception that, if a thought is not rational, it is necessarily irrational. This strict separation into rational and irrational is a false dichotomy. Some thoughts are *nonrational*, being neither rational nor irrational.

We say we are thinking rationally when we infer conclusions correctly. When we infer conclusions incorrectly, we say we are thinking irrationally. However, not all thinking is inference.

Introduction

Emotions, for example, are not inferences. When you desire a cupcake, you are not making an inference. You are not reaching a conclusion about whether the cupcake is a healthy eating choice or whether the cupcake might be stale. You are not even reaching a conclusion about whether you value eating the cupcake more than you value the alternatives. Instead, an emotion is a fact about your body and your brain. Because emotion is not an inference, it is neither rational nor irrational.

To illustrate this more clearly, let's make an analogy between being rational and being grammatical. We are being grammatical when we correctly construct sentences in speech and writing. When we incorrectly compose sentences, we are being ungrammatical. When we are eating lunch or appreciating fine art, we are being neither grammatical nor ungrammatical because we are not composing sentences at all. Likewise, when a person engages in thought or activity that is not inference, they are being neither rational nor irrational.

Obviously, blind rage or euphoria can short-circuit human reasoning ability, but our emotions are not in themselves irrational. A rational person is free to feel joy, sorrow, and anger as long as these emotions do not pervert their reasoning ability.

Value judgments, emotions, perceptions, and diversions are all nonrational. We are free to enjoy ourselves, make moral judgments, and enjoy the scenery without necessarily feeling that we are being irrational.

Now that we have this category of nonrational thinking, we can untangle a common confusion. Mr. Spock, the ultra-rational alien from the Star Trek TV series, is the popular media's poster child for the rational being. Spock is not only emotionless, he also considers anything outside of his duties to be a sin against logic. Despite Spock's alleged perfection, audiences perceive a kind of paradox. The very human Captain James T. Kirk is frivolous in comparison with Spock, yet the Captain always seems to have the winning strategy. How can Spock's perfection fail to be better than the Captain's in the eyes of the audience?

The confusion arises from the implicit assumption that Spock's value system is an integral part of his rationality. Spock clings to a spartan interpretation of human value, free of emotion, joy, and desire. However, Spock's values are not only nonhuman, they are also nonrational. One does not need to share Spock's values to be good at making inferences. Spock might argue that his values benefit group survival and social cohesion, but survival and cohesion are also nonrational values. While humans share these values, humans also value freedom, autonomy, and a life well lived. As such, winning for humans and winning for Vulcans (like Spock) mean two different things.

Reason is a tool that we use to get what we deem to be important. As David Hume put it, reason is "the slave of the passions."[2] We should regard rational thinking as akin to mathematical skill. When we improve our mathematical skill,

---

[2] David Hume (1740). *A Treatise of Human Nature*, Section III.

we do not become any less human. Quite the contrary. The better our mathematical ability, the better our ability to predict the future and the outcomes of our potential actions.

1.11   Inference Versus Behavior

In the last section, I stated that the terms "rational" and "irrational" describe acts of inference. However, in common parlance, the expression "acting rationally" applies to behaviors that are not acts of inference. For example, we would say that a man who abandons a sinking ship is acting rationally, or a man who pays his bills is acting rationally. Yet, acts such as climbing into a lifeboat or signing a bank check are not acts of inference. What we really mean, of course, is that acts like abandoning a sinking ship or paying bills are rationally justified behaviors. We mean that such behaviors are sanctioned by rational inference.

Following through on rational decisions is an important part of instrumental rationality. However, because this book is focused on epistemic rationality, I apply the words rational and irrational exclusively to rational inference. By this standard, actions that follow from rational inference are neither rational nor irrational.

1.12   Textbook Rationality

Critical thinking emphasizes a broad set of cognitive virtues, including the ability to look at systems and problems from new perspectives, intellectual humility, fairness, and communication. Critical thinking courses teach logical fallacies and help students locate errors and distortions in arguments and source materials.

There are two approaches to teaching critical thinking in schools. Whether by choice or by necessity, educators usually embed critical thinking prompts into their specialized classes. For example, a history teacher can ask her students to read multiple interpretations of a historical event and critique the author for biases and intent. In mathematics, an instructor can teach students to understand why a formula works and how to apply it in novel cases that do not at first appear mathematical. Some educators believe that critical thinking relies on background knowledge dependent on context, and critical thinking in science or geography can best be taught in their respective classes.

The other approach to teaching critical thinking is to teach a dedicated course on the subject. In this method, students are taught generic skills for analyzing problems, gathering information, checking sources, and avoiding logical errors. By cultivating general reasoning abilities, the hope is to create students who can be rational regardless of domain.

Introduction

Given that there is a method of reasoning that is both ideal and generic, I believe it makes more sense to teach a dedicated course which combines critical thinking and ideal rationality. I call this approach *textbook rationality* to distinguish it from traditional critical thinking courses. This name underscores the intended shift from soft skill rationality to technical rationality.

Figure 1 illustrates the relationship between textbook rationality and traditional critical thinking. Conventional critical thinking emphasizes best practices, human factors, and deductive reasoning. Ideal rationality concerns not only deductive reasoning, but general epistemology and inductive inference as well.

Educators have been developing their critical thinking toolbox for decades, and the scope of their existing techniques and experience far eclipse the relatively narrow topics in these pages. Rational thinking, as I describe it here, is not a replacement for the panoply of critical thinking resources that have been amassed to date. Rather, I see ideal thinking as the most neglected topic in critical thinking. To me, teaching critical thinking without teaching the principles of ideal rationality is like teaching students composition without ever explicitly teaching grammar. By teaching ideal rational thinking as part of critical thinking, students learn the universal rules for correctness.

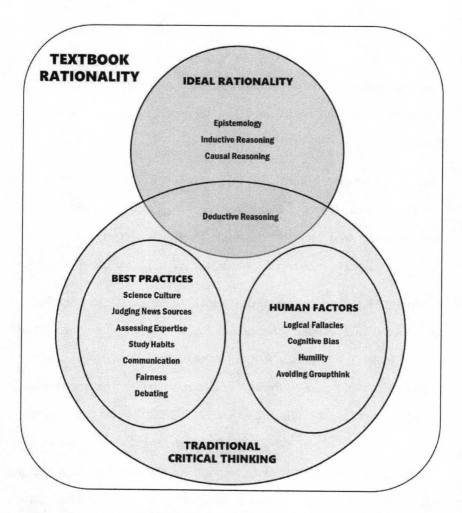

Figure 1: Textbook Rationality and its relationship to traditional critical thinking

1.13 Rationality Education

Rationality is vital to almost every academic discipline and human endeavor. Yet, the percentage of students who take a course on formal rationality is nearly zero. Overwhelmingly, students pass through high school with no explicit training in rational thinking at all.

Rational thinking is a matter of making correct deductive and inductive inferences. I will explain deduction and induction in the next chapter, but we can think of *deductive* inference as the application of rules and *inductive* inference as the discovery of rules. There are formal yet simple methods for making both types of inference. However, the modern understanding of rationality is new, having been developed in the 20th century. Formal rationality is not taught in schools because it is a relatively recent invention, and most teachers are unfamiliar with it.

To be fair, schools often teach two subject areas related to rationality. First, high school mathematics involves examples of deductive reasoning. Performing proofs in geometry and algebra gives students plenty of experience with deduction, even if they are not taught the general concept of deductive reasoning. Second, as discussed in the previous section, teachers endeavor to bring critical thinking to the classroom. However, the existing school syllabus falls far short of teaching critical thinking, let alone rational thinking.

Education currently fails at teaching rationality in four ways. First, the system makes little or no mention of rationality itself. People leave school without knowing what rationality is, what types of inference exist, how rationality relates to emotion, or what the limitations of rationality are.

Second, schools focus almost exclusively on deductive reasoning, ignoring inductive reasoning almost entirely. The few programs that teach critical thinking teach logical fallacies, but logical fallacies are fallacies of deductive logic, not inductive logic. Science is primarily a process of inductive inference, but as we shall see, science classes do not teach inductive inference.

Third, there are no formal courses or qualifications in rational thinking. This may seem like a minor point, but I will argue that it might make all the difference in the world.

Finally, schools fail to teach students rational due diligence and the best practices they will need for thinking clearly.

A complete course on rational thinking should cover:

- The concepts and philosophy of rationality—what rationality is and why it is important

- Ideal rationality—how an ideal mind would reason

- Cognitive bias—how humans fail at reason

- Techniques for overcoming our biases

I hold that the first two elements are the most important. Students should know what rationality is and how it is executed. Critical thinking makes much more sense when we place it in the context of ideal rationality. Critical thinking is how we get back on rational track after our cognitive biases throw us off course. From this point of view, teaching critical thinking without even mentioning rationality is downright peculiar. Moreover, I suspect that critical thinking skills will be much more coherent when framed as a salve for irrationality than as a laundry list of techniques.

Though this book is not a textbook, I roughly follow the course outline presented above. After discussing the philosophy of rationality, I will cover ideal reasoning and present some applications. Finally, we will move on to cognitive bias and countermeasures.

1.14   A Suitable Skepticism

You likely agree that rationality is important, and that human survival is threatened by our rationality deficit. However, there are reasons to be skeptical that rationality education is the solution to the problem.

I do not cling to the naïve hope that students of rationality will emerge from their courses as perfect reasoners. Not all students will master the subject after one course, and even the best students will find rationality difficult to apply in every domain. Studies show that we are all much better at finding the flaws in the arguments of others than our own. In some cases, education may even backfire, with students using their training to mint rational-sounding excuses to stick to irrational beliefs.

However, there are several reasons to believe dedicated rationality education will be a transformative innovation. First, a course on rational thinking is also a course on critical thinking. There is compelling evidence that dedicated critical thinking courses are an effective way to improve students' general thinking ability.[3,4]

Second, a course on rationality includes important topics that today's critical thinking courses omit, especially inductive reasoning. Failed inductive reasoning

---

[3] Abrami, Philip & Bernard, Robert & Borokhovski, Eugene & Waddington, David & Wade, C. Anne & Persson, Tonje. (2015). *Strategies for Teaching Students to Think Critically: A Meta-Analysis.* Review of Educational Research. 85. 275-314. 10.3102/0034654314551063.

[4] Tiruneh, Dawit Tibebu & Verburgh, An & Elen, Jan. (2014). Effectiveness of Critical Thinking Instruction in Higher Education: A Systematic Review of Intervention Studies. Higher Education Studies. 4. 10.5539/hes.v4n1p1.

is the primary reason so many people adhere to faulty beliefs. For example, the conspiracy theories that are often the subject of fake news are deductively consistent but inductively inconsistent. If we teach only deduction, it should not surprise us when students are blind to inductive reasoning errors.

Third, to the extent that human rationality is inherently limited, and to the extent that our limitations are an existential risk to our civilization, we need to develop new practices and technologies to overcome those limitations. These technologies might be built from software and artificial intelligence, or they may be new social institutions and standards. In either case, before we can solve the problem, we must name it. We cannot expect a new generation of graduates to solve a problem they do not know exists. We also need a workforce that is equipped to develop these new technologies, or at least know how to use them properly. Teaching rationality names the problem and explains what new technologies must do behind the scenes to solve the problem.

Last but not least, a course on rational thinking can change the culture. Culturally, formal rationality is not part of our discourse. Rationality is vaguely and informally understood by the average citizen. To the extent that rationality is used as a critique of belief, we generally hold ourselves to a depressingly low standard. People are rarely asked if their belief is rational, and if they are asked, they will give themselves a passing grade if they can invent any post hoc explanation for their belief. In this sense, we live in a prerational society. The cultural standard of rationality must be redefined to align more closely with the formal definition.

I like to make an analogy with scientific versus prescientific society. We consider our society to be scientific, the scientific revolution having occurred between the Renaissance and the late 19th century. We have a shared and somewhat formal definition of science. We get qualifications and certifications in sciences at the high school and college levels, and we have scientific standards of due diligence. Now, imagine you are living in the Middle Ages, without the modern meaning of the word science and without modern scientific qualifications. One day, you come across a monk trying out a new fertilizer in his vegetable garden. The monk plants identical types of vegetables in comparable plots of soil, with his usual fertilizer in one plot and the new fertilizer in the other. By comparing the growth in the two plots, the monk will have shown whether his new fertilizer is beneficial or detrimental. How clever! In our modern vernacular, the monk is attempting to perform a controlled trial of his new fertilizer. Without medieval words or concepts for science, how would you describe this monk and his methods?

You would probably call him clever—because you do not have a better word for what he is doing. Suppose you want to apply the same kind of cleverness to the breeding of ponies on your farm. How will you find someone of comparable skill? Will you post a bill in the town square seeking a clever man? How will you know that candidates answering your call have the right kind of scientific cleverness?

After all, there are many forms of cleverness, and innate scientific cleverness is extremely rare, even among geniuses.

If you can figure out how to generalize the methods of the clever monk, you could bring this new way of understanding the world to every industry and field of study. To teach the masses how to think scientifically, you would need to invent a word for science, give students a conceptual outline of scientific inference, and establish schools and standards of scientific aptitude.

The leap I envision, from scientific thought to rational thought, is smaller than the leap from medieval thought to scientific reasoning. Even if public education had existed in the 16th century, no one had formulated the vocabulary or scientific method well enough to teach scientific thinking. Today, we have a ready-made educational system and the conceptual and technical understanding of rationality ready to teach. All we need are teaching materials—and the vision to teach the subject matter.

The cultural goal would be to raise the standard of rational due diligence, in both public discourse and personal reflection. Until we do this, the scientific revolution is not truly complete. Science has not reached its full potential until citizens have the rationality skills to responsibly interpret science stories in the media.

1.15 A Place in the High School Syllabus

Teachers are busy. They have government mandates to teach reading, writing, and mathematics, and school performance is measured by standardized tests. Topics outside the core are squeezed by these demands. Given the pressures that schools are under, how can space be made for a course on rationality? Further, which department would teach classes in rationality? Mathematics? Science? Social studies?

I believe these follow-up questions about where to position the course suggest an interesting answer to the original query. A course in rationality is a course in all these subjects.

Rationality is at the core of scientific inference, and applied rationality often takes the form of a scientific investigation. From this perspective, science courses are ideally placed to teach the subject. On the other hand, ideal rationality is primarily an exercise in probability and statistics, and there is plenty of mathematical skill that can be taught along the way. The idea that high school students should be taught more probability and statistics instead of calculus has been circulating for some time now.[5]

---

[5] Sarah D. Sparks (May 2018). *Move Over, Calculus. Statistics Is on the Rise.* Education Week. Vol. 37, Issue 32, Pages 12-13.

Introduction

When it comes to the study of human irrationality, we study cognitive biases, the domain of psychologists. In learning about psychological experiments, human biases, and the extraction of insight from data on humans, students are learning about social science.

Thus, a course on rationality is a course in the sciences, social sciences, and mathematics. This suggests an obvious solution: Students can take a single course on rationality while earning credits toward requirements in all three domains.

Equally obvious is the immense challenge of making such a change to the standard syllabus. The solution is easier than adding a completely new required high school course, but it still requires considerable collaboration between departments, and possibly between schools and governments. Nonetheless, the political arguments for doing nothing do not stack up against the risk of continuing to graduate students who do not know how to reason.

2 DEFINITIONS

2.1 Consistency and Contradiction

The goal of rationality is to arrive at a logically consistent set of beliefs about the world. Logical consistency means the avoidance of contradictions, both in our beliefs and in our methods for forming those beliefs.

In its simplest form, consistency means that we should not simultaneously believe that a statement is true and false in the same way at the same time. For example, if I simultaneously believe that I am both sitting on the beach and not sitting on the beach, I am logically inconsistent in my beliefs. In practice, we do not tolerate such direct contradictions, though we sometimes entertain seeming contradictions by using different standards of truth for the contradictory claims. For example, I could say that if I am sitting on a towel at the beach, I am not sitting directly on the beach, and that I am therefore "sitting on the beach" and "not sitting on the beach" at the same time. Of course, to create this apparent contradiction, I was merely being ambiguous about what it means to "sit on the beach."

Real contradictions are more likely to creep into our beliefs when we have multiple, related beliefs. For example, consider the following set of statements:

a)   Bob will attend the conference at the Manhattan office on Monday morning.

b)   After a party in the evening, Bob always returns to his home in Queens and sleeps in past noon the next day.

c)   Bob is attending a party on Sunday night.

Taken together, this set of statements results in a contradiction. If Bob attends a party on Sunday evening, he will sleep in past noon, so he will be sleeping at home on Monday morning, not at the office conference. The statements (b) and (c) imply Bob will not be at the office conference on Monday, contradicting statement (a). Yet we might not notice the contradiction between the beliefs until we are sitting in the office conference room on Monday morning, wondering why Bob has not arrived. If we can miss a contradiction hidden in just three beliefs, imagine how easy it might be to miss a contradiction lurking among dozens or even hundreds of beliefs.

The existence of a contradiction poisons the entire set of beliefs. We saw how statements (b) and (c) led us to conclude "not (a)," contradicting (a). Starting from any two of our statements, we can prove the third is false. For example, we can start from statements (a) and (b) and conclude "not (c)," contradicting (c). If we believe Bob will attend the conference on Monday morning, and Bob always sleeps in after a night out partying, we should also believe Bob must not be partying on Sunday night. It turns out that a single contradiction in any set of statements leads to the absurd conclusion that every statement is simultaneously true and false. Logicians call this the "principle of explosion."

Obviously, we wish to avoid contradictory beliefs so we can avoid blowing up our entire system of beliefs. Logic was invented as a mathematical tool for showing how statements are related to each other and for proving that a set of statements has no contradictions.

2.2   Inference

Simply put, rationality is about making proper inferences. Inference is a process that derives new conclusions from evidence, assumptions, and existing beliefs. We infer whenever we make a judgment about our world. When we make judgments, we update our beliefs about the way the world is, and about what we can expect in the future. Inference is the process that creates human knowledge.

Our most profound judgments concern our choice of career, investments, national policy, philosophy, and choice of spouse. Yet even the most trivial judgments—updating our beliefs about the weather forecast or what we should eat for dinner, for example—rely on rudimentary rationality.

By studying rationality, we seek a kind of unified theory of judgment that will guide us in understanding all the judgments we make—a theory that can explain why one judgment is better than another judgment. Happily, a universal theory of judgment does exist.

The idea of a general theory of judgment is not an obvious one. The types of reasoning we use in science, mathematics, and in navigating personal relationships all seem distinct from each other. Even within mathematics, we have many tools in our toolbox. Yet there are general principles of reasoning that apply everywhere. When we understand the general principles, we can see every instance of reasoning as a context-specific application of the general rules.

2.3 Deductive and Inductive Inference

Roughly speaking, inference consists of two activities—applying general principles and discovering general principles—and we classify inferences into two corresponding types: *Deductive* inferences concern the application of rules, whereas *inductive* inferences are attempts to find out what the rules are.

For example, if you read and accept the rules of a simple board game, deduction can tell you what moves are legal and perhaps tell you what moves are most likely to win the game. In contrast, if you are learning how to play a game merely by watching others play it, you are using inductive inference to figure out the rules of the game.

This board game example helps us see deduction and induction in other contexts too. When scientists perform experiments and examine their outcomes, they are attempting to discern the rules that nature plays by. Thus, experimental science is mostly inductive. In contrast, when an engineer applies well-tested laws of physics to verify a new engine design, they are applying known laws of nature and performing a deductive task.

To be rational, whether in business, government, or your private life, you must predict the outcomes of your actions based on what you know as well as learn from outcomes of past actions. These two activities roughly correspond to deduction and induction, respectively.

Deduction and induction are complementary and equally important forms of reasoning. Deduction is simpler and more familiar. Induction is more challenging and the form of reasoning most overlooked by our educational system.

2.4   Deduction: Avoiding Contradictions

Among college reasoning courses, the term "logic" usually refers to a calculus for performing deductive reasoning. Mathematicians have devised several forms of symbolic logic, including propositional logic, predicate logic, and modal logic. At first glance, each form of logic seems like an impenetrable discipline, filled with strange-looking symbols and theorems. Yet, for all its complexity, there is a simple principle that defines what logic does: logic is a formal method for avoiding contradictions.

Deductive logic applies general rules, ruling out possibilities that would contradict them. Consider the following inference:

Premise 1: All men are mortal.

Premise 2: Socrates is a man.

Conclusion: Socrates is mortal.

This particular chain of reasoning is known as the Socrates syllogism. Its conclusion follows intuitively from the premises, but let's put aside our intuition and ask why the conclusion necessarily follows. If we conclude that Socrates was immortal, our conclusion would contradict one of the premises. Either Socrates is not a man, or not all men are mortal. The conclusion must be correct, or we have a contradiction.

Deduction is a general method that discards possibilities that contradict accepted rules. When we deduce correctly, alternative conclusions are impossible, for they would violate the accepted rules. For example, once we accept the rules of arithmetic, we must conclude that $25 + 36 = 61$. Any other answer is logically impossible because it would result in a contradiction. Deduction is about logical consistency.

2.5 Valid and Sound Arguments

As we have seen, deduction operates in the context of rules and premises, inferring conclusions that are necessary to avoid contradictions. However, the rules and premises of a deductive argument need only be true hypothetically—for the purposes of argument. The process of deduction operates as if the word "if" appears before each premise or rule. *If* all men are mortal, and *if* Socrates is a man, then Socrates is mortal.

Because deduction is a general way of following rules, we can use deduction with whatever rules we find useful or entertaining. When playing chess, we are implicitly accepting and obeying the rules of chess, and deduction keeps us from making illegal moves or expecting illegal moves from our opponent. When playing checkers or bridge, the rules will be different, but in the context of each game, we accept the rules of that game to make our deductions.

We say a deductive argument is *valid* when the conclusion follows from an assumption of the premises and rules. Thus, we can say the following argument is valid:

Premise 1: Mammals nurse their young.

Premise 2: Ostriches are mammals.

Conclusion: Ostriches nurse their young.

These statements are consistent with each other, so the deduction is correct, given the premises. Such an inference is valid. However, the premises are not true because ostriches are not mammals.

When we believe the rules and premises of a valid argument are true, and not merely hypothetical, we describe the argument as *sound*. For example, the following argument is both valid and sound:

Premise 1: Birds lay eggs.

Premise 2: Ostriches are birds.

Conclusion: Ostriches lay eggs.

2.6   Induction: Learning From Experience

Deduction can tell us whether a set of statements is logically consistent (i.e., free of contradictions) and whether an argument is logically valid. However, deduction cannot tell us whether an argument is sound or whether a premise or a conclusion are actually true. To differentiate between truths and hypothetical truths, we need another form of inference: induction.

In Chicago, we have rain in summertime and snow in wintertime. Precipitation is in the form of snow if the temperature is cold enough and in the form of rain if the temperature is above about 35° Fahrenheit. On a warm summer day in Chicago, you will not observe precipitation falling as snow. The fact that snow only falls in cold weather is a rule that nature plays by. How did we come to know this fact?

We began by noticing patterns of association—snow is associated with cold temperatures. The pattern was so consistent that we eventually took the pattern to be a rule that we can use to make deductive inferences. Pattern matching is a crude form of inductive inference. Nonetheless, pattern matching is often effective at establishing matters of fact.

2.7   The Principle of Induction

Inductive inference enables us to discover the rules that best explain our observations, and once we have inferred those rules, we can use our knowledge of those rules to deduce predictions about future observations.

With the notable exception of mathematics and computer science, our knowledge consists primarily of facts and conclusions drawn from experience and observation. Everything we know about the world around us, about our friends and our neighborhood, we know by finding patterns in our observations, and by assuming that these patterns will persist into the future. This assumption, that the past is a guide to the future, is called *the principle of induction*. Although this principle seems obvious to us, philosophers have yet to come up with a proof that it is justified. We cannot use past successes we have had with the principle to argue that the principle will hold in the future without assuming the principle we are trying to prove.

This problem of induction has long troubled philosophers. Epistemology is the philosophical study of knowledge, and the ultimate goal of epistemologists is to provide a deep explanation for how we know what we know. If induction is based on an unjustifiable assumption, does that mean our knowledge is unfounded?

Not exactly. All rational arguments and proofs implicitly assume rational principles. Consequently, it is impossible to create rational arguments for the principles of rationality without creating a circular argument. Thus, the failure to find a noncircular proof for a rational principle is what we would expect of any rational principle.

The principle of induction is a rational principle. It has the same status as the rational principles that undergird deductive reasoning.

2.8   The Process of Induction

Humans are natural learners, and we often make inductive inferences subconsciously. However, subconscious induction is error-prone. We seek a technical description of what an inductive inference ought to look like. We want a systematic description that makes each part of the process clear.

Induction is a five-step process:

1. **Observation**—observe events.

2. **Abduction**—devise one or more theories that, if they were true, would explain the observed events.

3. **Prediction**—for each theory, make predictions about what we would likely have observed.

4. **Test**—compare the events we have observed to the predictions of each theory.

5. **Update**—reapportion our confidence in each theory based on how well the predictions matched our observations.

Learning from experience begins with experience. The observations in step (1) can be any kind of experience, from a visual observation, scientific measurement, or any other kind of distinct experience.

Second, abduction is the creative task of devising theories that might explain the observations. The candidate theories suggested by abduction compete for the best available explanation for our observations. Candidate theories are sometimes profound and complex. Sometimes they are nothing more than the continuation of a simple pattern.

Third, we take each of our theories and use them to predict what our observations ought to have looked like if each theory were true. Interestingly, this step is deductive. Assuming the rules of our theory are true and predicting the necessary consequences that follow is a task that predicts specific consequences from general rules. The process of induction relies on these deductive inferences.

Fourth, we test the predicted observations against our actual observations using a mathematical score. In the next chapter I explain how this mathematical scoring is performed and why it is justified.

Finally, we increase our confidence in the winning theory based on its score on the test.

2.9   Classifying Tasks as Deductive or Inductive

Classifying activities as either inductive or deductive is complicated by the interplay between the two kinds of inference. To make an inductive inference, we need to use deduction to tell us what the candidate theories predict. To make sound deductive inferences, we need to rely on inductive inferences to tell us which general rules are true and not merely assumed.

The distinction between induction and deduction is clearer the more we zoom in on a task. The more we zoom out, the fuzzier the distinction becomes. Commonly, science is considered an inductive task because the goal of science is to infer the general rules by which the universe operates. However, many tasks scientists undertake are deductive. When a scientist is exclusively concerned with step three in the process of induction, they are making deductive inferences. In such cases, scientists may write entire papers making predictions based on theories that are assumed to be true.

Engineering may be thought of as deductive. Engineers do not determine the rules of physics and chemistry. Rather, they apply the rules to solve problems, like building bridges or designing engines. Applying rules of known theories is primarily deductive. However, many engineering tasks are not so simple that they can be solved by deduction alone. Indeed, making predictions from a known theory is often difficult, and engineers need to create and test their own theories, just as scientists do. There are equations that tell us how air flows around a supersonic jet, but these equations cannot be solved exactly for objects as complex as an airplane. Engineers need to run experiments in a wind tunnel or in a computer simulation to find out how a given airframe will respond at different speeds and orientations. In such cases, engineers are performing inductive inferences, much the way scientists do.

In mathematics and science classes, we often encounter purely deductive tasks. Consider the following question:

If I drop a mass from the top of the Tower of Pisa (183 feet above the ground), how fast will the mass be moving when it strikes the ground?

To solve this problem, a physics student applies known laws of motion and the known acceleration due to gravity. All the student needs to do is plug the relevant numbers into a pair of equations.

In research, we sometimes undertake explicitly inductive tasks. Suppose you want to know whether a drug effectively treats a disease. You should understand the normal progression of the disease and compare that normal progression against the progression of the disease after treatment. This sort of experiment relies on inductive inference, most of the induction occurring at the conclusion of the experiment when the data is analyzed.

Everyday life is filled with inductive inferences, most of which is implicit and subconscious. For example, imagine you are seated on a moving train, and the man sitting next to you says, "That green is pretty." He could be talking about the scenery outside the window, the color of the green bag you are carrying, or something else entirely. Each of these possibilities represents a theory that makes different predictions. If he is talking about the scenery, you expect to look out the window and see something with a pretty, green color. If he is talking about your luggage, you expect to see the man gesture or glance at your bag. Based on your observations, you will grant more confidence to one theory over the other.

Similarly, you just used your powers of induction to learn about the word for, and the concept of, induction. Induction is pervasive. You have been using induction since before you entered school as a young child and have probably lived your entire life without any explicit training in induction. You know how to make inductive inferences without knowing how they are supposed to be made.

2.10   Hypothesis, Theory, and Fact

You may have heard a critic deride a theory by exclaiming, "That's just a theory!" Indeed, in common English, we often use the word theory as a synonym for a guess or a hypothesis.

Yet, you may also have heard scientists explain to laypeople that a scientific theory can be a fact. How are we to reconcile the multiple uses of the term "theory"?

Theory is the general term for a model that makes predictions about observations. We may use other terms to describe a theory based on our degree of justified confidence in the theory.

A hypothesis, or conjecture, is simply a theory which has insufficient evidence for us to grant it high confidence. When we have sufficient evidence to raise our confidence in a theory to an extremely high level, we refer to that theory as a fact. When a theory lies somewhere between hypothesis and fact, we usually refer to it as a theory. A fact is a well-justified theory. A hypothesis is an as yet unjustified theory.

2.10.1 Example Fact: Special Relativity

Einstein's special theory of relativity tells us how matter and energy behave in flat spacetime. The special theory tells us that the speed of light is the same for all observers, and mass and energy are equivalent through Einstein's most famous equation, $E = mc^2$. Decades of experiments have verified that the theory predicts our observations to high accuracy. Thus, we say that the special theory of relativity is a fact.

2.10.2 Example Hypothesis: RNA First

RNA First is a theory about the first cellular life on Earth. Life needs a mechanism for replicating itself, and the RNA First theory proposes that life could have started replicating using RNA instead of the more complex process of DNA-to-RNA replication. This theory has appeal because much of the molecular machinery in biological cells is made of the same stuff as RNA. However, there are other theories competing for best explanation of the first life, and RNA First does not have enough evidence to strongly distinguish itself against its competitors. As such, we might refer to the RNA First theory as a hypothesis.

2.10.3   Example Theory: Inflationary Cosmology

Between these two extremes are theories that have confirming evidence, but not so much evidence that we would be shocked to see them overturned. For example, according to inflationary theories, for a tiny fraction of a second after the Big Bang, our universe underwent a period of extreme expansion. This rapid expansion accounts for the observation that the leftover glow from the Big Bang is extremely uniform across the sky. Experimental tests have confirmed some key predictions of this cosmic inflation, so cosmic inflation is more than a hypothesis. However, there are many models of inflation, and we know little about the underlying mechanism of the theory. Thus, physicists do not yet grant the theory of cosmic inflation so much confidence that they would regard it as a fact. Instead, cosmic inflation looks like the best explanation for our observations and a solid basis for future research.

2.11   What Science Courses Omit

The scientific method is a form of inductive reasoning. Science is a disciplined way of learning from experience wherein scientists make a conscious effort to be careful in their inferences, keeping careful track of evidence and attempting to account for uncertainties. However, we must not confuse scientific practice with a formal understanding of inductive inference.

In practice, the scientific method is a cultural phenomenon. Scientists do not generally have training in formal rational inference. Instead, science relies on the scientific community's social conventions which are conducive to scientific progress. Scientists are cooperative, publishing results in journals, explaining their reasoning, and describing their experiments so that other scientists can analyze and replicate their findings. Scientists are also adversarial, critiquing each other's theories, competing to publish the best explanation of phenomena, and racing to be the first to make a discovery. Science is a game of social status wherein social status is ultimately based on explanatory success.

A typical high school science education reflects this cultural approach. High schools teach the scientific method using flowcharts like the one in Figure 2.

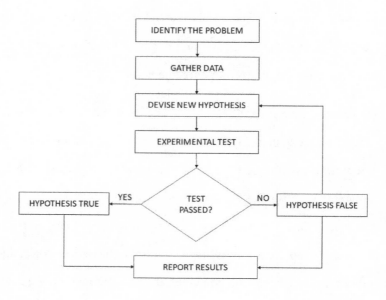

Figure 2

Figure 2 represents the cultural practice of science. Superficially, it resembles our process of induction. What the flowchart lacks is the meaning of the terms "test" and "analyze." How do we know when a hypothesis is "true"? How do we know when a theory passes a test?

We teach students how to perform experiments, following in the footsteps of the great experimentalists in history. Many of history's most famous science experiments have obvious and intuitive interpretations. For example, Galileo observed phases of Venus that were impossible in the Earth-centric theory of the solar system. Galileo also showed that the rate at which an object falls to Earth is independent of its mass, in clear contradiction with the reigning theory of his day, which stated that heavier objects fall faster. In unequivocal cases such as these, theories pass or fail tests in obvious and intuitive ways. Such examples implicitly teach students that they can rely on their intuitions to interpret scientific results.

However, unequivocal experimental outcomes are the exception rather than the rule. More typically, multiple competing theories can explain data, and the challenge is to weigh the evidence and identify which theory is most likely to be correct. In other words, the goal of science is to make rational inferences from evidence to conclusion.

Proper rational inference is a technical, quantitative process. In contrast, qualitative, intuitive judgments sometimes work, but they sometimes fail. Until we teach students the technical process, we will not succeed in teaching them to be scientifically literate.

In the next chapter, I discuss formal methods we can use to weigh evidence. Students who lack awareness of these methods are liable to misinterpret the results of studies.

3   THE IDEAL

3.1   Ideal Reasoning

In the first two chapters, I laid out the "why" and "what" of rational thinking. In this third chapter, I will describe *how* we should reason. Specifically, our goal is to describe the proper method of inductive reasoning.

Recall that deductive reasoning tells us the consequences of a theory or set of rules, whereas inductive reasoning tells us which of our theories is more likely to be true given the available evidence. Put another way, deductive reasoning tells us what we should expect to observe if a theory is true. Inductive reasoning tells us what is true based on what we actually observe.

The marvelous thing about the reasoning technique you are about to learn is that it is both simple and universal. However, before we can reason formally, we need a brief discussion about probability.

3.2   Probability

The general concept of probability is familiar to all of us. We associate probability with a degree of expectation about future events. Though we may have an idea of what probability means, almost everyone is prone to make mistakes when using probability to understand the world or predict the future. This book is not a substitute for a book on probability and statistics, but we will discuss the concept of probability in a way that will reduce confusion and prepare us for using probability in reasoning.

3.2.1   Epistemic Probability

When reasoning, we are interested in epistemic probability. Epistemic probability concerns what we as observers expect to see. Knowledge is expectation. When we know something, we are saying we expect some future observations to be more likely than other observations. Because we are flawed observers, we have access to only a limited amount of information about our surroundings, but the more we observe, the more we learn about our world by updating our expectations.

Expectations can be quantified by using frequencies, i.e., with numbers that say how many times we expect to see a particular outcome in a given number of trials. For example, in 100 rolls of a 10-sided die (100 trials), we expect the number nine will appear 10 times (10 expected events). In terms of frequency, we could say that we expect 10 events in 100 trials.

Probability gives us one more way to quantify our expectations, but in terms of a single trial. Instead of saying, "we expect a frequency of 10 events in 100 trials," we can say, "the probability of an event in a single trial is 10 per 100—10% or 0.1."

3.2.2   Combining Probabilities

Most of us are already comfortable with probabilities. If there is a 5% chance that our airline flight will depart today, we understand that our flight is unlikely to leave today, even if we do not think to ourselves that out of 20 comparable trials, our flight would only depart in one of them.

We usually become confused when asked to combine probabilities together. However, the rules are simple. Simply put, we multiply probabilities whenever we compute the overall probability of an event given the probabilities of the partial steps or prerequisites for that event.

Suppose we are booking a last-minute flight from New York to Rome, with a layover in London. To get to Rome this way, we have to acquire a ticket from New York to London and a ticket from London to Rome. Suppose there is a 90% chance we can find a seat on a flight from New York to London, but only a 50% chance we can find a seat on a flight from London to Rome. What is the combined probability that we can find seats on both legs of the trip?

In this problem, we are calculating the coincidence of two probabilities, finding a seat on both legs at the same time. Thus, we need to multiply these probabilities together. The probability is 90% x 50% = 45% that we can acquire a seat on both legs of the flight.

If we ever get confused when working with probabilities, we can usually straighten ourselves out by recasting the problem in terms of frequencies. If the last example is unclear, express the problem in terms of frequencies. Out of 100 attempts to find a seat on a flight from New York to London, 90 will succeed. Out of 100 attempts to find a seat on a flight from London to Rome, only 50 will succeed. So, out of 100 attempts to find a seat on both legs of the journey, how many will succeed?

Imagine that we make 100 attempts to find seats for the journey. Of the 100 attempts to book the New York to London leg of the trip, 90 out of every 100 succeed. Of the 90 attempts that make it to London, 50% of the attempts to find a seat on the flight to Rome succeed. That means 45 out of the 90 attempts that made it to London will find a ticket to Rome. 45 divided by the original 100 is 45%.

3.2.3 Probability Distributions

Since we cannot have fewer than 0 nor more than 100 events in 100 trials, we grade probability on a scale of 0 to 1, or 0%–100%. This allows us to relate probabilities using a bit less information than we might otherwise have needed.

In our last example, we computed that there was a 45% probability that we could find seats on a flight itinerary from New York to Rome. What is the probability that we would not be able to find an available itinerary?

Since there is a 100% chance that we will either find an itinerary or not find one, and there is a 45% chance that we will find one, it must be the case that there is a 55% probability that we will be unable to find seats on both of the flights we need.

When an outcome is a fact or foregone conclusion, we grant it a probability of 100%. In the example, though it is unknown whether we will find our flights to Rome, we know it is a foregone conclusion that we will either find our flights or not find them. This 100% of our probability must account for the mutually exclusive possibilities. Thus, if there is a 45% chance of finding our itinerary, the remaining 55% of the probability must be distributed such that it accounts for the mutually exclusive and complementary possibility that we do not find flights to Rome. This the simplest example of what is called a *probability distribution*. A probability distribution is an accounting for everything we know about how a necessary or factual result came (or will come) to pass. A probability distribution assigns a share of the 100% probability to each mutually exclusive path to the outcome.

Consider a six-sided die. If we roll the die, we know the outcome will be 1, 2, 3, 4, 5, or 6. That is, the probability of rolling any number from 1 to 6 is 100%. (Let's ignore outlier cases where the die lands on an edge, shatters into a powder, etc.) However, because our six-sided die is fair, we have no reason to believe any particular face of the die is more likely to appear when we roll the die. Thus, our probability distribution is one in which 100% is distributed equally into six mutually exclusive outcomes, each with a probability of 16.66%.

In the case of the ideal six-sided die, we define the probability distribution to have six equal buckets of probability. In some cases, we discover probability distributions by collecting statistical information. For example, academic testing companies collect information about how students score on standardized tests. From this information, they can derive a probability distribution that tells us what score to expect when a random student takes the test. For example, in such a distribution, the number of students attaining the maximum score is fewer than the number of students attaining an average score.

3.2.4 Knowledge and Probability

At the beginning of this chapter, we stated that knowledge is expectation. If knowledge is expectation and probability distributions map out our expectations, we can map out our knowledge using probability distributions.

It is common to associate the term "knowledge" with statements about which we are certain. However, certainty is elusive. For any given claim, we would have to have performed an infinite number of tests, checks, and verifications before declaring it certain. In practice, certainty is unnecessary. We only need to be confident enough in our knowledge to be comfortable completing our task.

When we build an airliner, we do not need to be certain of our physics and engineering before we are comfortable flying aboard our jet. As long as our estimate of the probability of an accident is low enough, we will be happy to fly aboard the jet. Likewise, every time we do a confirmatory experiment or successfully recheck our formulas, we become more confident in our knowledge. Eventually, we assess the probability of our error low enough to declare that we know the formulas, know the engineering, and know the reliability of our work.

Of course, there is always the possibility that we have made some sort of error or that we have been lulled into a false sense of security by unfortunate circumstances. In the 1998 film The Truman Show, the main character lives out his life in the artificial world of a reality TV show. The story is far-fetched, but it illustrates one of the possible ways that we could be mistaken in our knowledge of the everyday world.

How are we to give up certainty yet avoid the paranoia that we might be mistaken about everything? When the confidence in our knowledge is well-justified, we have all the certainty that is required. As we shall see, the probability that major errors and conspiracies corrupt our most reliable knowledge is extremely small.

3.2.5   Probability Distributions and Randomness

Once we have a probability distribution, we can simulate expected observations by using random picks from the distribution. The probability distribution for the flip of a fair coin has two buckets, one for heads and one for tails. Each bucket contains 50% of the probability. To simulate flips of a coin, imagine that we represent each percentage point of the distribution by a colored ball, 50 red balls representing 50 percentage points for tails and 50 yellow balls representing 50 percentage points for heads. We put all 100 balls into a bin and shake it. We then draw a ball from the bin at random. By this method, we simulate what happens when we flip a coin.

To simulate the next flip of the coin, we again pretend we have a bin of 100 balls representing the fair distribution. We never draw a second time from the same bin (i.e., each time we draw from the bin containing 100 balls).

The graph in Figure 3 gives a probability distribution of heart disease by age. In other words, if a physician tells you they diagnosed a new patient with heart disease, the probability distribution tells you the probability that this new patient lies in a specified age range.

Since our distribution is using whole percentages, we can represent the probabilities using 100 balls with colors corresponding to the age ranges in the distribution. Thus, we would have 18 green balls labeled "18–44," 32 yellow balls labeled "45–64," etc. To simulate what it is like to observe an event with this distribution, we imagine drawing a ball at random from our bin of 100 balls. When the physician tells you they diagnosed a new patient with heart disease, your expectation that the patient was aged 45–64 is equivalent to your expectation that a yellow ball would be drawn at random from the bin of 100 balls.

The Ideal

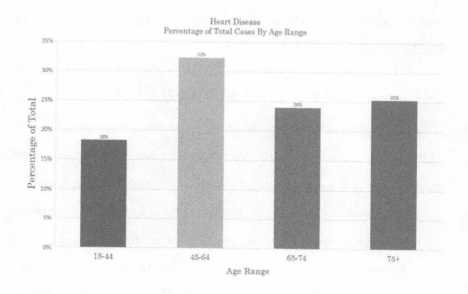

Figure 3
Source: CDC, National Center for Health Statistics, Summary Health Statistics Tables for U.S. Adults: National Health Interview Survey, 2018, Table A-1b, A-1c.

Everything we know about the world is encoded into a probability distribution. What we measure is then a random draw from that distribution. If it were not epistemically random, we would be admitting that we knew how to make a better probability distribution.

Much of our knowledge is probabilistic in this way. Sometimes, we know only what statistical patterns we expect to see but are unable to predict the exact observations themselves. Perhaps there is no better illustration of this than quantum electrodynamics (QED). QED is the most precise predictive theory ever developed. Yet QED makes statistical predictions. We can accurately predict the

65

probabilities of events in our experiments without being able to predict exactly which event will occur.

3.2.6   Deductive, Empirical, and Inferred Probability

We use probability distributions to represent our models of the world. Distributions may be pictures of what the world is like to the best of present knowledge, or they may be pictures of what the world might be like in a theory or model. If a distribution represents a picture of reality as we know it, we obtain the probability distribution by making observations of the world and making inferences from the observations. On the other hand, if a distribution is a picture of the way the world might be, we arrive at the distribution by following whatever rules define our theory.

When we devise a theory, we are devising a probability distribution, either implicitly or explicitly. This probability distribution represents what we expect to observe if the theory is true. We typically infer distributions using deductive methods.

When we make statistical observations, we are measuring the probability distribution empirically. For example, scientists determined the probability distribution for heart disease incidence as a function of patient age by statistical observation.

By definition, a perfect six-sided die has an equal chance of landing on any of its six sides. By deduction, therefore, the probability distribution for rolls of such a die grants one-sixth or 16.66% of the probability to each of the six possible ways the die could land. However, the average physical, six-sided die will likely have manufacturing imperfections that make some faces of the die slightly more likely to appear than other faces. The way to determine this distribution is to roll the die repeatedly and see what theory best fits the results.

The challenge of inductive inference is this: Which theory best fits our past observations, yielding the best predictions about the future?

In terms of probability distributions, the challenge of inductive inference attempts to look at observations and infer which theoretical probability distribution is the best match to reality. Amazingly, it turns out that we can do better than determine which theory fits best—we can infer how much credence to give to each competing theory, and even determine how much each observation ought to shift our degree of belief.

3.2.7   Expected Values

Once we have a probability distribution, we can compute what we expect to observe over the long run. A fair coin has a probability distribution for each flip of 50% heads, 50% tails. If we flip a fair coin four times, how many heads and tails should we expect to see?

To get a statistically expected value, we multiply the probability times the number of flips. Four flips times 50% heads give us two instances of heads, and four flips times 50% tails give us two instances of tails. Hence, we expect to see heads appear twice and tails to appear twice, on average.

Of course, in any actual series of four flips, we may not see two of each kind of outcome. For example, even with a fair coin, we might see heads-heads-heads-tails or tails-heads-tails-tails. However, in the long run, we expect the number of sequences in which heads outnumber tails to be the same as the number of sequences in which tails outnumber heads. If we were wagering on the number of heads that we would see in a sequence of four flips, we should bet that there would be two. We would sometimes lose this bet, but it would be the best bet that we could make.

To give just one more example, if we know only that it rains in Los Angeles 36 days out of the year, we know that the probability of rain on a day in Los Angeles is about 10% per day. If a visitor is staying in Los Angeles for 10 days, we should statistically expect it to rain on one day during their stay (10% x 10 days = 1 expected day).

3.3   Bayesian Reasoning

Bayesian reasoning is named after a famous theorem in probability theory. In the late 18th century, Reverend Thomas Bayes was trying to solve precisely the problem outlined above. Given multiple theories with differing probability distributions, how should we update our confidence in the respective theories given new evidence?

Ingeniously, two constraints help us solve this problem. First, if one of our theories is true, the sum of the probabilities of our theories being true must add up to 100%. Suppose a patient either has heart disease or does not have heart disease. If there is a 25% chance that the patient has heart disease, there must be a 75% chance that the patient does not have heart disease (25% + 75% = 100%). Consequently, if evidence reduces our confidence that the patient has heart disease to 20%, it raises our confidence that the patient does not have heart disease to 80%.

Second, the order in which we receive evidence about the world should not matter to our eventual conclusion. Imagine a physician opening a packet of information about a patient. The packet contains a dozen different pieces of evidence relevant to the patient's case: patient history, EKG, stress test result, blood test results, etc. Some evidence may nudge the physician's diagnosis in favor of heart disease while other evidence may reduce their confidence in that diagnosis. Obviously, the physician's confidence in a heart disease diagnosis will go up or down as they pull each new piece of data from the patient's file, and their confidence at any given time during the review will depend on which order they read the evidence. However, no matter which order the physician reads the information from the patient's file, they should reach the same conclusion after they have read all the information in the file and taken all evidence into account.

Bayesian reasoning proceeds in steps, like our hypothetical physician. As each piece of evidence arrives, the reasoner updates their confidence in each theory, subject to the constraint that the probabilities of each theory being correct must sum to 100%. At each step, there are two inputs: the reasoner's prior confidence in each theory and the predictions each theory makes about what evidence is likely to appear. The output of each step is the updated (or posterior) degree of confidence in each theory.

Instead of diving into mathematics, we will describe a simple game that illustrates the principles of Bayesian reasoning.

3.4   Six-Twenty: A Dice Game

Six-Twenty is a simple dice puzzle that explains how we ought to update our beliefs in response to evidence. The game illustrates three insights about inductive inference. Every time we make a judgment based on new evidence, we are implicitly playing an analogue of this game.

3.4.1   Round 1

In Six-Twenty, I have a six-sided die and a 20-sided die.[6] To begin the game, I select one of the two dice at random.

What is the probability that I selected the six-sided die?

---

[6] Following modern usage, I will use the word "dice" as both singular and plural noun.

In the terms we developed earlier, I am asking you to estimate your rational confidence in the theory that I selected the six-sided die. In this game, there are only two theories—the six-sided die theory and the 20-sided die theory—and the theories are mutually exclusive.

Initially, since I selected my die at random, and there are only two dice, the probability I selected the six-sided die is 50%.

Next, I roll the selected die. I tell you I rolled a three.

You now have more information, more evidence. What is the probability I selected the six-sided die?

To solve this problem, we will use the statistically expected results of playing multiple games. If I roll a six-sided die six times, I statistically expect to see each of its sides come up exactly once, on average. Imagine we repeat this game 120 times.

Figure 4 is an illustration of the statistically expected results of playing 120 games. In 120 games, I would first pick a die at random. Since my choice is random, I expect to select the six-sided die 60 times (i.e., 50% of the 120 games). Similarly, in those 120 games, I would choose the 20-sided die 60 times. Of the 60 rolls of the six-sided die, I expect to roll a 3 an average of 10 times. In 60 rolls of the 20-sided die, I expect to roll a 3 just three times. Thus, in 120 games, I expect to roll a 3 a total of 13 times, 10 of those times on the six-sided die.

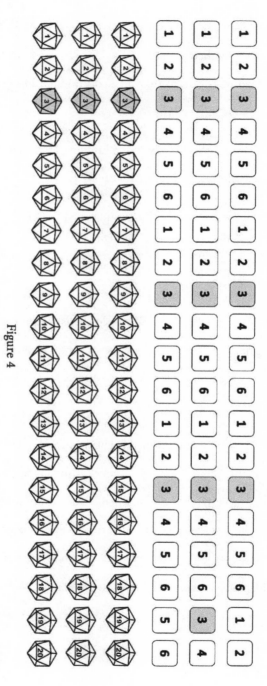

Figure 4

120 games of Six-Twenty. Since the choice of die was random, we expect 60 rolls of the six-sided die and 60 rolls of the 20-sided die. I have highlighted the expected instances of rolling a 3.

From this, we can calculate what we ought to expect if this particular game is representative of a typical game of Six-Twenty. When I roll a 3, you should expect the six-sided die was selected 10 in every 13 times, or about 77% of the time.

This result represents an application of the first principle of rational inference. The asymmetry in the predictions of the two theories gives us information about which theory is probably correct. The 20-sided die theory is more flexible in that it allows for more possible outcomes than the six-sided die theory. The six-sided die theory is more restrictive, and it makes a narrower prediction. If the six-sided die theory is true, it spreads its prediction probabilities across just six outcomes. If the 20-sided die theory is true, it spreads its probability across 20 outcomes.

If the number rolled on the die is in the range 1 to 6, the six-sided die theory will be a more successful theory. The 20-sided die theory is more flexible, but that flexibility is a weakness when the theory wastes that flexibility on outcomes that never materialize.

> **Insight 1: Inferential advantage goes to the theory that is the least flexible while still accounting for the data.**

3.4.2   Rounds 2–14

Suppose I keep the same die I selected in the first round and roll it another 13 times. I read off each of my rolls as they happen: 6, 2, 2, 3, 4, 1, 6, 5, 4, 5, 1, 1, and 3.

You now have 13 additional pieces of evidence from which to draw a conclusion. What is your revised estimate for the probability that I selected the six-sided die?

Obviously, you are much more confident that I selected the six-sided die than you were after the first round. This new data overwhelmingly confirms the six-sided die theory. In fact, if you estimate the odds of rolling a number in the range 1–6 on the 20-sided die 14 rounds in a row, you should expect this to occur only once in a sequence of 20 million rolls.[7] This provides a high justification for believing that I selected the six-sided die.

This brings us to the second insight about rational inference:

Insight 2: Justification for a theory can accumulate.

3.4.3   Round 15

Suppose I roll my selected die one more time. This time, I tell you I rolled a 14. What is your revised estimate of the probability that my selected die was the six-sided die?

---

[7] The probability of rolling a 1, 2, 3, 4, 5, or 6 on a 20-sided dice is 6/20 or 30%. To roll 1–6 on a 20-sided die 14 times in a row is a coincidence, so we must multiply all 14 instances of the 30% probability. $(30\%)^{14} = 0.0000000478$. This small probability goes into 1 about 20,907,516 times.

The intuitive answer is zero; you are now certain that I had originally selected the 20-sided die and that a string of unlucky data points previously misled you into believing otherwise.

However, our previous theory was extremely well-established. You believed that the six-sided die theory correct to something like one part in 20 million. To say this theory is false is quite an extraordinary claim. Is there a way that your new data point could be wrong?

Assuming we are both dedicated to playing the game according to our rules, there is still a way your data could be faulty. If I misread the die, misstate my reading, or if you mishear my reading, your data could be wrong. These are highly improbable events. Let's suppose that the rate of making such an error is one in one million rounds. At that rate, if playing this game were a full-time job, it would still take us more than half a year to commit this error even once. My guess is that such errors occur much more frequently than this. Nonetheless, the low error rate of one in one million rounds is still much higher than the one in 20 million rate at which a 20-sided die will produce results like a six-sided die for 14 rounds in a row. In other words, after seeing a number in the 1–6 range 14 times in a row, a single data point to the contrary is not enough to displace our preference for the six-sided die theory.

This illustrates a third insight about rational inference:

Insight 3: Extraordinary claims require extraordinary evidence.

The reader may wonder whether I have changed the rules of the game to rig this surprise at the end. I can assure you I have not. To verify this, we shall apply this theory of error to the first round.

In the first round, when we rolled a 3, we computed that there was a 10/13 chance that the six-sided die theory was correct. An error rate of one in one million does not significantly change this result. Such a small error rate would change our initial estimate from 76.9231% to 76.9230%—not enough to concern us.

Similarly, had we rolled a 14 on the first round, we would have concluded that there was a 0% chance that the six-sided die theory was correct, assuming no error in the data. Accounting for a one in one million possibility of error, we would revise our estimate of the probability that the six-sided die theory is correct upward from 0% to around 0.0001%. Again, not a revision that would significantly alter our estimate on the first round.

Extraordinary claims do require extraordinary evidence, but extraordinary evidence is not qualitatively different from any other kind of evidence. Extraordinary evidence is nothing more than evidence that is sufficiently abundant to counterbalance the evidence to the contrary, even after we have accounted for the likelihood of faulty data.

In summary, we can boost our confidence in a theory to high levels by amassing evidence. When our confidence in a theory becomes extremely high, we rationally regard any competing theory that comes along as extraordinary because the competing theory must not only account for any new evidence, but also for the evidence that we amassed previously. We need an extraordinary amount of new evidence to justify the new theory because the new evidence must outweigh the extraordinary amount of old evidence.

3.5   Six-Twenty and Bayesian Reasoning

Six-Twenty is more than a mere demonstration of statistical reasoning. Every time you make a rational judgment based on new evidence, you are playing a game analogous to Six-Twenty. Your judgment may be akin to choosing between more dice with more sides and with different numbers printed on them, but the basic principle is the same.

A note to the math-averse:

To express Bayes' rule and get best use out of it, we need to use a little bit of algebra. However, there is no need to panic! You will not need to solve any equations. Using Bayes' rule is just a matter of plugging numbers into the formula. Indeed, you can get a lot of value out of the formula without putting numbers into it. Just use it as a shorthand. For example, you will see me write "P(X)" as a shorthand for "the probability of X."

In this section, I will explain Six-Twenty visually and introduce the shorthand. Later, we will get to the equation and apply it in some examples. If the math becomes too challenging for you, please press on. You can learn a lot by following the arguments and examples, even without the math.

Bayes' theorem is the mathematical generalization of the Six-Twenty game. If you have followed the Six-Twenty game, you have already grasped the fundamental ideas behind Bayesian reasoning, the gold standard of inductive inference. To become fluent in the language of Bayesian reasoning, you will need to learn the notation. Although I will use some formulas, I hope the diagrams should make the formulas seem intuitive.

Bayes' rule follows from the fact that, for some possibilities, there is a total probability of 100% that something will happen. In the Six-Twenty game, there is a probability of 100% that either the six-sided or 20-sided die will be chosen. I will represent the total probability as a rectangular box:

WHAT CAN HAPPEN (100%)

We can think of this box as representing all the possible worlds we might be living in. In Six-Twenty, before any die is thrown, there are two kinds of worlds we might be living in, worlds where the six-sided die was selected and worlds where the 20-sided die was selected. Since the selection was random, we say that the six-sided die was selected in 50% of these possible worlds and the 20-sided die was selected in the other 50% of worlds.

6-sided die selected (50%)	20-sided die selected (50%)

These two 50% probabilities are called *prior* probabilities. They are the probabilities that either theory is true before we consider new evidence. Let's call the six-sided die theory D6 and the 20-sided die theory D20. Then we express this initial state as:

$$P(D6) = 50\%$$

$$P(D20) = 50\%$$

We can further subdivide these possible worlds into worlds where each possible roll of each die appears:

1	2	3	4	5	6	1	2	3	4	5	6	7	8	9	10	11	12	13	14	15	16	17	18	19	20

Notice that the 50/50 proportion is preserved, but each side is now subdivided according to possible outcomes of a roll of the die. Since the six-sided die has fewer possible outcomes, each segment of the six-sided possibility is larger than the size of the roll outcomes for the 20-sided die.

The sizes of these segments are the predictions of each theory. For example, the probability of rolling a 1 on the six-sided die is 1/6 the probability in worlds where the six-sided die was selected. Similarly, the probability of rolling a 3 on the 20-sided die accounts for 1/20 the probability in worlds where the 20-sided die is selected.

The ratio of the size of the segment to the total size of all the segments for a given theory is called the *likelihood*.

Likelihood of 3, Given D6 =

"$P(3|D6)$"

The standard notation for a likelihood is expressed on the right. P(3|D6) is symbolic for "the likelihood of rolling a 3 given a world where D6 is true."

We can visually represent the likelihood of rolling a 3 on the 20-sided die in a similar way:

Likelihood of 3, Given D20 =

"$P(3|D20)$"

Of all the worlds we might be living in, not all of them will be compatible with observations that we make. When we observe our world, we filter out some of the possibilities that used to exist. For example, if we observe that a 14 was rolled on the selected die, we must be living in a world where rolling a 14 is possible. Ignoring the possibility of a bad observation for the moment, this means that we live in the set of possible worlds in which a 14 was going to be rolled.

The following diagram represents this scenario. When a 14 is rolled, only those possible worlds which predicted 14 would be rolled next survive the observation filter.

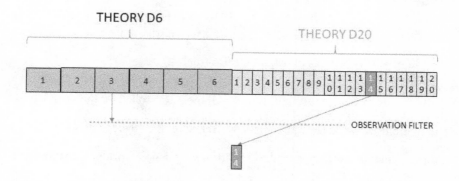

In what fraction of these surviving possible worlds was the 20-sided die rolled? 100%, of course. Therefore, we conclude that a 14 implies we live in one of the worlds where the 20-sided die was selected, and theory D20 is true.

Now, let's consider how this would play out if a 3 were rolled instead of 14. Because both the six-sided die and the 20-sided die have a 3 on them, some of each world survives the observation filter.

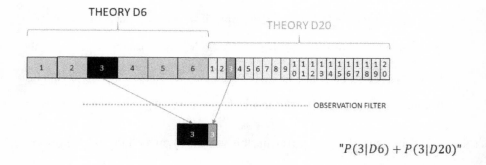

$$"P(3|D6) + P(3|D20)"$$

In the standard notation of Bayesian reasoning, the total size of the surviving segments is equal to the sum of the two likelihoods, P(3|D6) + P(3|D20).

What Bayesian reasoning does next is to ask, "In what fraction of the possible worlds that survived this observation is D6 true?"

There are more possible worlds in which the 3 was rolled on the six-sided die than there are worlds in which the 3 was rolled on the 20-sided die. The sizes of these segments faithfully track the proportions of possible worlds compatible with the observation. After making an inference from our evidence, the probability that we are in a world where the six-sided die was selected is the following ratio:

Probability of D6,
Given roll of 3   = $\dfrac{3}{3\quad3}$ $"P(D6|3)"$

This is the answer we have been looking for, the probability that the D6 theory is true given the observation of a 3. In Bayesian language, this is called the *posterior* probability that the D6 theory is true given the observation of a 3, and the symbol for this quantity is P(D6|3). Expressing this probability as a ratio formula, we have:

$$P(D6|3) \ = \ \frac{\boxed{3}}{\boxed{3}\ \boxed{3}} \ = \ \frac{P(3|D6)}{P(3|D6) + P(3|D20)} \ = \ \frac{\frac{1}{6}}{\frac{1}{6} + \frac{1}{20}} \cong 77\%$$

This formula is simpler than the general case because we started with equal prior probabilities; i.e., we started with the D6 theory and the D20 theory being equally probable, P(D6) = 50% and P(D20) = 50%.

All we need to do to derive the more general Bayesian formula is to consider another roll of the die. We started out with equal prior probabilities. After we observe that a 3 was rolled on the die, the two theories are no longer equally probable. For round two of Six-Twenty, our posterior probabilities become our new priors. For round 2:

$$P(D6) = 77\%$$

$$P(D20) = 23\%$$

In the second round, we again subdivide the D6 part into six equal segments and subdivide the D20 part into 20 equal segments. The next roll of the die is 2:

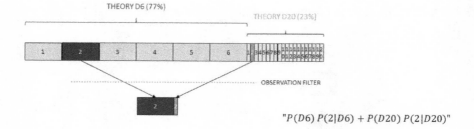

"$P(D6) P(2|D6) + P(D20) P(2|D20)$"

Again, our observation filter passes forward only those possible worlds that predicted a 2. Some of these worlds are from D6 and some are from D20. How large is the surviving segment from D6?

It is the size of total D6 rectangle times the likelihood of rolling a 2. The likelihood of rolling a 2 on D6 is 1/6, and the size of the total D6 rectangle is just the prior probability of D6.

In symbols, the size of the surviving dark-shaded segment is:

$$P(D6)P(2|D6)$$

Similarly, the size of the surviving lighter-shaded segment is:

$$P(D20)P(2|D20)$$

Thus, the total size of the surviving rectangles is:

$$P(D6)P(2|D6) + P(D20)P(2|D20)$$

Clearly, after 2 is rolled, an even larger proportion of the surviving possible worlds is worlds in which D6 is true. Calculating this proportion tells us the new posterior probability that the six-sided die was rolled given the roll of 2 (after the roll of 3), P(D6|2).

Probability of D6, Given roll of 2 (round 2) = $"P(D6|2)"$

We have all the numbers we need to compute this:

$$P(D6|2) = \frac{P(D6)P(2|D6)}{P(D6)P(2|D6) + P(D20)P(2|D20)} = \frac{77\%\frac{1}{6}}{77\%\frac{1}{6} + 23\%\frac{1}{20}} \cong 92\%$$

After rolling 3 and then 2, we are now 92% confident that the six-sided die was selected.

The formula in the diagram above is the Bayesian updating formula we have been looking for. If we have two theories, T_1 and T_2, and we receive some new evidence, E, then we can calculate the posterior probability that T_1 is true given the evidence E:

$$P(T_1|E) = \frac{P(T_1)P(E|T_1)}{P(T_1)P(E|T_1) + P(T_2)P(E|T_2)}$$

This is an astonishing formula. We go through our lives making gut assessments of evidence to determine what we believe. Yet here is a formula that tells us exactly how we ought to update our confidence in a theory as a function of new evidence.

Of course, we are rarely in a situation where we have exact numbers for our prior probabilities and likelihoods. However, this formula is profoundly useful. As we will see, there are many cases where our natural human instincts are so far off the mark that Bayes' formula is far superior. Moreover, the structure of this formula gives us a guide to understanding everything from human psychological biases to the scientific method.

3.6   Standard Notation

In the previous section, I informally introduced Bayesian notation. In this section, I will describe the terminology in more detail.

3.6.1   Two Notations for Probabilities

The first expression in this notation is simply $P(X)$, which means the probability of X. X may refer to a theory or a piece of evidence, and the meaning is a little different in the two cases. If X is a theory, T, then $P(T)$ means the probability that theory X is true. We already encountered this notation when expressing the prior probability (e.g., $P(D6)$). If X is a piece of evidence, E, then $P(E)$ represents our estimate for the likelihood of seeing that piece of evidence, no matter which theory is true.

The second kind of expression in standard notation is called *conditional probability*. $P(X|Y)$ means "the probability of X given Y." We read the vertical line as "given that." We saw this in the last section. $P(3|D6)$ meant the probability of seeing 3 given D6, and $P(D6|3)$ meant the probability that D6 was true given the appearance of 3.

This notation is more compact than plain English, and easier to understand, too. Now that we have a standard notation, we can talk about the concepts more generally.

3.6.2   Theories and Likelihoods

A theory specifies the likelihood of finding a piece of evidence. For example, the D6 theory specifies the likelihood of each roll of the die appearing.

The theory that a patient has Type 1 diabetes makes predictions about what will happen when we look at that patient's medical history, blood chemistry, and genetic background. For example, we expect with 100% probability that a patient with Type 1 diabetes who fasts overnight will still have high blood sugar in the morning. We would say, "The likelihood (probability) of seeing the evidence (high blood sugar after overnight fasting) given that our theory (Type 1 diabetes) is true is 100%." This is a conditional probability because it is the probability of seeing some evidence, conditioned upon the theory being true. Thus, in standard notation, this statement is expressed as:

P(high fasting blood sugar|Type I diabetes) = 100%

Similarly, we can apply this notation back to the theories in our Six-Twenty game.

Test Yourself

Satellite XY1 is in an unknown, decaying orbit. We do not know when it will re-enter the Earth's atmosphere. What is the likelihood that XY1 will re-enter the atmosphere on a Thursday?

What is the likelihood that XY1 will re-enter the atmosphere during the night?

How would you express these likelihoods in standard notation?

3.6.3   Priors

The goal of Bayesian reasoning is to update our degree of confidence in our theories in response to a new piece of evidence. This step-by-step process takes as its input an estimate of our confidence in each of our theories prior to evaluating the evidence. These initial estimates are called *prior probabilities*, or simply *priors*. Our priors for a new cycle of Bayesian reasoning are the outputs of the previous cycle of Bayesian reasoning.

Recall that if we have 100% confidence that one of our theories is correct, the sum of our confidence in each of our theories must add up to 100%. If we have two theories and assume at least one of our theories is correct, the more confidence we have in one theory, the less we have in the other. In the special case where we have no more confidence in one theory than the other, we believe that each theory has a 50% chance of being correct. This is precisely the situation we saw in Six-Twenty. Initially, one of the two dice was selected at random. Thus, prior to receiving any evidence from rolls of the die, we know there is a 50% probability that the six-sided die was selected and a 50% chance that the 20-sided die was selected. Our prior probabilities are 50% and 50%, respectively. In standard notation, we would write:

$$P(D6) = 50\%$$

$$P(D20) = 50\%$$

3.6.4 Posterior Probability

After we evaluate a new piece of evidence, we will update our estimates for the probabilities that each of our respective theories is true. These probabilities are called *posterior probabilities* because they are calculated after we evaluate the evidence. Posterior probabilities will become our prior probabilities when we receive further evidence and enter the next cycle of Bayesian reasoning.

Posterior probabilities are conditional probabilities because they represent the probability that a theory is true given some new piece of evidence. In standard notation, a posterior probability is written as:

$P(T|E)$

or, the probability that theory, T, is true given the evidence, E.

For example, the probability that a patient has Type 1 diabetes given the evidence that they have high fasting blood sugar is written as:

P(Type I diabetes | high fasting blood sugar)

Similarly, in Six-Twenty, the posterior probability that the six-sided die was rolled given that the outcome was a 3 is written as:

P(D6|3)

This notation is like the notation used for likelihood, but the meanings are different. A likelihood, P(E|T), represents our knowledge about what a theory predicts. A posterior probability, P(T|E), represents our best estimate that a theory is true given the evidence.

3.6.5   The Probability of Evidence

What is the probability that we will observe a given kind of evidence based on our current information and confidence levels? For example, based on information we possess, what is the probability that a 3 will be observed on the next roll of the die while playing Six-Twenty? The answer to this question depends on two factors, the likelihood of observing a 3 in each of our theories and our prior confidence in each theory.

If we are playing Six-Twenty, and we have 99.999% prior confidence that the six-sided die is in play, we expect there is about a one in six chance that a 3 will appear. On the other hand, if we have 99.9999% prior confidence that the 20-sided die is in play, there is approximately a one in 20 chance that a 3 will be observed on the next roll.

If this is the first roll in a game of Six-Twenty, and we have no more confidence in either die being in play, both theories contribute to the probability that we will observe a 3, in proportion to our respective prior confidence in each theory. In round one of the game, based on the limited information we possess, we calculate the probability of observing a 3 as:

$$P(3) = P(D6)P(3|D6) + P(D20)P(3|D20)$$

$$= 50\%\, P(3|D6) + 50\%\, P(3|D20)$$

$$= 50\%\, \frac{1}{6} + 50\%\, \frac{1}{20}$$

$$= \frac{13}{120}$$

$$= 10.83\%$$

We can also determine the probability that we will observe a 15 in round one as:

$$P(15) = P(D6)P(15|D6) + P(D20)P(15|D20)$$

$$= 50\%\, P(15|D6) + 50\%\, P(15|D20)$$

$$= 50\%\, 0 + 50\%\, \frac{1}{20}$$

$$= \frac{1}{40}$$

$$= 2.5\%$$

We can double-check that we are on the right track by considering the probability of observing any roll from 1 to 20 during the first round of a game of Six-Twenty. Adding the probability of the individual outcomes must add up to 100% since we assume that we will certainly observe one of the 20 numbers. There are six outcomes possible on both dice (calculated like P(3)), and 14 outcomes possible on the 20-sided die (calculated like P(15)). Adding them up, we get:

$$P(any\ number) = 6\ (10.83\%) + 14\ (2.5\%)$$

$$= 65\% + 35\%$$

$$= 100\%$$

As expected!

Generalizing our formula, we can say that the probability of seeing a particular piece of evidence is the sum of the products of the likelihoods and priors:

$$P(E) = P(T_1)P(E|T_1) + P(T_2)P(E|T_2)$$

When there are three theories, the formula would be:

$$P(E) = P(T_1)P(E|T_1) + P(T_2)P(E|T_2) + P(T_3)P(E|T_3)$$

And so on.

3.6.6   Bayes' Theorem

Bayes' theorem tells us how to update our confidence levels based on new evidence. Although the theorem looks technical, it simply tells us how to update our confidence just as we did in the Six-Twenty game.

Recall that in the game, we updated our confidence levels by calculating the ratio of the probability of arriving at our observations assuming a theory were true divided by the total probability of arriving at those same observations across all possible theories. In standard notation, Bayes' theorem is as follows:

$$P(T_1|E) = \frac{P(T_1)P(E|T_1)}{P(E)}$$

$$= \frac{P(T_1)P(E|T_1)}{P(T_1)P(E|T_1) + P(T_2)P(E|T_2)}$$

where T_1 and T_2 are our two theories, and E is the new evidence we have received.

Technically, the theorem tells us how to calculate the posterior probability from our priors and likelihoods. This formula is simpler than it looks, and we can get to know the formula better by looking at some special cases.

In round one of Six-Twenty, when $P(D6) = P(D20) = 50\%$, the formula simplifies to:

$$P(T_1|E) = \frac{P(T_1)P(E|T_1)}{P(E)}$$

$$P(D6|3) = \frac{P(D6)P(E|D6)}{P(D6)P(E|D6) + P(D20)P(E|D20)}$$

$$= \frac{50\% \, P(3|D6)}{50\% \, P(3|D6) + 50\% \, P(3|D20)}$$

$$= \frac{P(3|D6)}{P(3|D6) + P(3|D20)}$$

$$= \frac{\frac{1}{6}}{\frac{1}{6} + \frac{1}{20}}$$

$$= 77\%$$

We calculated this same result intuitively in our original, intuitive analysis.

With Bayes' theorem, we can easily calculate our confidence level for round two. Going into round two, the only thing that changes is our priors. Instead of 50/50 priors, we have 77/23 priors. If we roll a 6 on round two, we calculate our posterior probability as follows:

$$P(D6|6) = \frac{P(D6)P(6|D6)}{P(D6)P(6|D6) + P(D20)P(6|D20)}$$

$$= \frac{77\% \, P(6|D6)}{77\% \, P(6|D6) + 23\% \, P(6|D20)}$$

$$= \frac{77\% \, \frac{1}{6}}{77\% \, \frac{1}{6} + 23\% \, \frac{1}{20}}$$

$$= 91.7\%$$

If we continue with this process, we will duplicate the same result we achieved after round 14 of Six-Twenty (i.e., our confidence in the 20-sided die theory will fall to less than one in 20 million.

Can Bayes' theorem account for our final round of Six-Twenty?

Recall that in the game, our final piece of data being in the range 14–20 was insufficient to overwhelm the prior data we had collected. After accounting for the possibility of error, we no longer estimated a zero probability for the six-sided die theory.

Yes, we can use Bayes' theorem to show that extraordinary claims require extraordinary evidence, but we need to modify our simple probability distributions to account for the possibility that poor data might be mistaken.

For the sake of argument, let's assume that the probability of making an error while reading, speaking, or hearing the die roll is one in one million, or 0.0001%. This does not affect our probability distribution for seeing results on the 20-sided die, since the probability of seeing any given result in the range 1–20 is still equal for all sides. However, the probability distribution for outcomes of the six-sided die needs to change because some of the probability has "leaked" into the range 7–20. There is a one in one million chance that we will observe a number greater than six, even though the six-sided die is being rolled. All the probabilities must add up to 100%, so we need to adjust the probability of rolling a 3 down from one in six a tiny amount to compensate. Still, we can perform this step-by-step calculation quite easily in a spreadsheet. Table 1 shows our results after each of the 15 rounds. As we can see, there is virtually no difference to the probability estimates in the early rounds. However, adding a one in one million probability estimate for error affects the result of the 15th round. As expected, hearing "14" on the 15th round lowers our established confidence in the six-sided die theory, but not to zero. Instead, it falls from 99.999995% to 96.76%. This is equivalent to a confidence level of about one in 30 that the 20-sided die theory is true.

ROUND	CONFIDENCE IN SIX-SIDED DIE AFTER ROUND
1	76.922828%
2	91.742907%
3	97.370876%
4	99.196464%
5	99.757572%
6	99.927147%
7	99.978133%
8	99.993439%
9	99.998031%
10	99.999409%
11	99.999823%
12	99.999947%
13	99.999984%
14	99.999995%
15	96.759772%

Table 1

3.7 A Bayesian Checklist

To reason in a Bayesian fashion, we identify the factors in Bayes' formula and put the corresponding numbers into the equation. In many cases, we do not even have to work with the numbers. Simply identifying all the factors is often enough to understand the basis of a scientific inference, find the exaggerations in a science article, or recognize the potential flaws in social policy. To help you apply Bayesian thinking, below is a checklist of steps to follow.

☐ **Identify the theories under consideration.**

What theories are we comparing?

Merely asking this question can be enough to avoid an error. Bayes' rule assumes that the theories under comparison are mutually exclusive. If the two theories we are comparing can both be true at once, our formulas will not work because the sum of probabilities that each theory is true can exceed 100%.

For example, are human character and behavior the result of genetics or of culture and socialization? Phrasing the question in this way suggests that the theories are:

a.   Human character is caused by biology.

b.   Human character is caused by culture.

If the theories really were this simple, experiments would easily distinguish which theory were true. Yet, in any realistic scenario, our character and behavior are determined by both genetics and culture, both nature and nurture. No one takes the two theories to be so simplistic, except for rhetorical reasons.

To make such a question more realistic, our theories must predict when genetics will be the strong determinant, and when culture will likely override our biological biases. These types of questions are much more difficult to answer with evidence.

Are there additional theories to consider? Bayesian reasoning can deal with multiple theories at once. We cannot always arrange for a theory and its counterpart to be the only alternatives. Is there a third option?

☐ Estimate the prior probabilities.

How much confidence do you have in each theory?

To get a starting point for your prior probabilities, you can use your gut. However, our instincts for making probability judgments are not very precise. If the probability in question is more than 95% or less than 5%, there is a good chance that a gut check will be far off the mark. Human brains do not intuitively grasp the difference between one in one million and one in one billion, for example. So, to get an estimate for a prior probability, you might need to consult some statistics.

For example, if you are going to be tested for a rare disease, you probably will not have an accurate or precise gut estimate for the prior probability that you have the disease. In such a case, you can consult statistics about the number of new cases diagnosed each year to estimate the prior probability that you are one of the new cases.

☐ Identify the evidence.

What is the evidence for the inference?

Perhaps the evidence is a medical test or government statistic. Perhaps it is an anecdote or trend. Depending on your information source, there is probably a bias of some kind, whether deliberate or accidental. Some opinion polls are biased toward a methodology or political point of view. Economic and social indices have respective strengths and weaknesses.

Remember: Evidence comes in the form of reports, and there are always ways that reports can be faulty. Even seeing something with your own eyes can be a faulty report to yourself. We are all subject to illusions and hallucinations, albeit rare.

☐ Calculate the likelihood of the evidence in each theory.

Statistically, what do the theories predict you will observe?

A piece of evidence can only distinguish between two theories when the theories make different predictions about the frequency of that evidence. The likelihoods, $P(E|T1)$ and $P(E|T_2)$, in each theory are the predictions of the theory, and our inference process is most productive when the likelihoods are dissimilar for each theory $P(E|T_1) \neq P(E|T_2)$.

In Six-Twenty, the likelihoods were not only different, they were also easy to calculate. Likelihoods are rarely so easy to assess.

☐ Anticipate false positives.

How can an experimental test mislead you with a positive result?

An experimental test for theory A is an experiment in which the likelihood of a positive result in theory A is high while the likelihood of a positive result in other theories is low. It is important to remember that the likelihood of a positive result in alternate theories is almost never zero. In Six-Twenty, if D20 was selected, you could still get a couple of rolls that are 6 or less. In effect, these rolls of D20 that are compatible with D6 are like false positives for the D6 theory. If you play Six-Twenty enough times, you will eventually see rounds where you are misled by false positives. Your analysis must account for them.

Moreover, even when a piece of evidence is naively impossible in one of the theories, it is rarely so when we look at the big picture. Again, this is because evidence consists of reports, and some reports are mistaken. The theory that "X does not happen" is not the same as saying that "X will never be observed or reported." In Six-Twenty, the naïve D6 theory says that rolling a 14 is impossible. Yet, as we saw, errors in observation and communication between the players could result in faulty reports, for example, hearing "14" instead of "4." Similarly, if aliens do not visit Earth, we should not expect that no one will ever report sighting alien visitors anyway.

☐ Extraordinary claims require extraordinary evidence.

Perhaps you have taken great care in setting up your experimental test. Your evidential test has a high true positive rate and a low false positive rate. You run the experiment and get a positive result. Does this prove your theory?

Not if you started with tiny priors. You may need to repeat the experiment multiple times to overcome small priors.

This often happens when testing for rare diseases. A good medical test might catch 98% of true positives and have a low, 1% false positive rate. But if the disease is extremely rare and only one in 10,000 people contract the disease, a positive test result means the patient still has approximately a 0.97% chance of truly having the disease. The probability has gone from a prior of 0.01% up to 0.97%. Running a second, independent test would get your confidence in the diagnosis up to 49%.

4   APPLICATIONS

4.1   Bayesian Reasoning in the Real World

Bayesian thinking and the Six-Twenty analogy make reasoning easier in a multitude of ways. Having an explicit formula for reasoning from evidence is profound. It means we can use Bayesian mathematics to double-check our intuitive beliefs. However, Bayesian reasoning is so much more than a formula. We can use Bayes' theorem as a mnemonic device, a map to help us locate errors about the world. When we make reasoning errors, we often do so by ignoring parts of Bayes' recipe or by failing to input the correct number into the formula.

Next, I will show you how to see Bayes' theorem in some real-world problems and how it can help you reason to better conclusions.

4.2   Bayesian Reasoning and Everyday Thinking

If Bayesian reasoning is a unified theory of reasoning, then correct, everyday inferences must be Bayesian, too. What kinds of things does the average person know, and how is their knowledge justified?

Much of what we know is justified by taking note of the frequency of events in experience. We notice that rain falls in warm weather, but snow only falls in cold weather. We notice that the sun rises every day. We notice that white automobiles are more common than pink ones. These observations inform our priors and conditional probabilities. We can write:

P(sunrise) = approximately 100%

P(snow|warm weather) = approximately 0%

P(pink car color) = approximately 0.2% (1 in 500)

P(white car color) = approximately 20%

Although we may not give any thought to snow in summertime or a day without a sunrise, such events are possible, and we should never formally permit our prior probabilities to equal exactly 0% or exactly 100%.

In everyday judgments, we typically use our background knowledge in conjunction with new pieces of information to update our beliefs. Suppose I tune into a new radio station and want to know what kind of music the station plays.

To make this assessment, I implicitly follow the Bayesian checklist from the last chapter. To begin with, I identify my theories: the station is a popular music station, a classical music station, a country music station, etc.

Next, I consider my prior probabilities. In my experience, most radio stations are more likely to play popular music than to appeal to niche listeners. Popular music appeals to more people, so radio stations can charge more for their advertising slots. In Bayesian terms, this translates into prior probabilities for radio stations playing music of different varieties. In a Northern U.S. city, my distribution of priors looks something like this:

P(pop music) = approximately 35%

P(dance music) = approximately 10%

P(hip hop and R&B music) = approximately 20%

P(Latin music) = approximately 15%

P(country music) = approximately 10%

P(classical music) = approximately 10%

For each type of station, I have expectations about what artists I am likely to hear. These are my likelihoods. For example, I am fairly likely to hear pop-country crossover star Taylor Swift on a country music channel or a pop channel, but I am unlikely to hear her music played on a classical or Latin music station.

Finally, I can update my confidence levels in each theory by applying Bayes' theorem. If I hear Taylor Swift being played:

$P(pop\ music|Taylor\ Swift)$

$$= \frac{P(pop\ music)P(Taylor\ Swift|pop\ music)}{\begin{array}{c}P(pop\ music)P(Taylor\ Swift|pop\ music)\\ + P(country\ music)P(Taylor\ Swift|country\ music)\\ +P(Latin\ music)P(Taylor\ Swift|Latin\ music)\\ +\cdots\end{array}}$$

I assume that the likelihood of Taylor Swift being played on anything other than country and pop music channels is approximately zero. Further, not knowing any better, I might assume that Taylor Swift is as likely to be played on a country music channel as on the pop music channel. With this assumption, my equation simplifies to:

$P(pop\ music|Taylor\ Swift)$

$$= \frac{P(pop\ music)P(Taylor\ Swift|pop\ music)}{\begin{array}{c}P(pop\ music)P(Taylor\ Swift|pop\ music)\\ + P(country\ music)P(Taylor\ Swift|country\ music)\end{array}}$$

$$P(pop\ music|Taylor\ Swift) = \frac{P(pop\ music)}{P(pop\ music) + P(country\ music)}$$

$$P(pop\ music|Taylor\ Swift) = \frac{35\%}{35\% + 10\%} = 77\%$$

In other words, the likelihoods cancel out, and my prior probabilities set my expectations. Based on my background knowledge, the station is probably a pop music station. Of course, if the next song played on the station is by pop star

Ariana Grande, my initial conclusion will be confirmed. If the next song is by country star Waylon Jennings, my initial conclusion will be overturned.

We make inferences like this every day, typically without explicitly invoking Bayes' theorem, but it is good to see our best intuitive judgments line up with a Bayesian approach.

4.3   Outperforming Intuition

At the best of times, we are Bayesian reasoners. However, the brain has evolved non-Bayesian shortcuts that save time and energy at the cost of accuracy. These shortcuts, or *heuristics*, lead to predictable biases. Consider the following question:

> Dave wears glasses and is an introvert. Is Dave more likely a salesperson or a librarian?

People tend to answer such questions by comparing Dave to the stereotypical image of librarians and salespersons. Dave is clearly a better match for the stereotypical image of a librarian, so we conclude that Dave is more likely a librarian than a salesperson. However, even if librarians fit the stereotype, which is far from obvious, the inference is faulty. To see why, we can phrase the question in Bayesian terms and run through our checklist.

We begin with our formula for the posterior probability:

$$P(T_A|E) = \frac{P(T_A)P(E|T_A)}{P(T_A)P(E|T_A) + P(T_B)P(E|T_B)}$$

This serves as a map and guide for our inference. All we need to do is fill in the values with what we already know. If we do not know what value to substitute for a symbol, we can make our best guess or do some research.

To start with, we identify the theories and the evidence, T_A, T_B, and E. The theories are:

T_A: Dave is a librarian.

T_B: Dave is a salesperson.

E: Dave wears glasses and is an introvert.

Next, we estimate our priors, $P(T_A)$ and $P(T_B)$. Prior to the evidence, which occupation is Dave more likely to have?

If we did not know that there are many more salespeople than librarians, we might say the prior probabilities are 50% for each. Yet, most of us correctly estimate that there are more salespeople than librarians. In the U.S., statistics show that there are about 50–150 times more salespeople than librarians. In other words, our prior belief should be that Dave is much more likely to be a salesperson than a librarian.

Assuming the prior probability that Dave is a librarian is 1% (and the prior probability that he is a salesperson is correspondingly 99%), we can write our Bayesian inference as follows:

$$P(T_A) = 1\%$$

$$P(T_B) = 99\%$$

$$P(T_A|E) = \frac{P(T_A)P(E|T_A)}{P(T_A)P(E|T_A) + P(T_B)P(E|T_B)}$$

$$= \frac{1\% \, P(E|T_A)}{1\% \, P(E|T_A) + 99\% \, P(E|T_B)}$$

Finally, we need to estimate the likelihoods. What is the likelihood that a salesperson wears glasses and is an introvert? What is the likelihood that a librarian wears glasses and is an introvert?

This is a difficult question to answer. Though we should expect them to be different, we have no compelling reason to think they differ greatly. Indeed, it has been estimated that between 33%–50% of people are introverts. For us to conclude that Dave is a librarian, we would have to believe that glasses wearing and introversion are about 50–150 times as common among librarians as among salespeople. This seems implausible.

To be generous to the librarian theory, let's assume there is a 50% likelihood that every librarian wears glasses and is an introvert. We make a similarly extreme assumption that only 10% of salespeople are glasses-wearing introverts. We now have enough information (or assumptions) to complete our Bayesian inference:

$$P(E|T_A) = 50\%$$

$$P(E|T_B) = 10\%$$

$$P(T_A|E) = \frac{1\% \, P(E|T_A)}{1\% \, P(E|T_A) + 99\% \, P(E|T_B)}$$

$$= \frac{1\% \, 50\%}{1\% \, 50\% + 99\% \, 10\%}$$

$$= \frac{0.5\%}{0.5\% + 9.9\%}$$

$$= 4.8\%$$

Thus, even with generous assumptions, it is about 20 times more likely that Dave is a salesperson. With this example, we have done far more than solve a toy puzzle. By using Bayes' formula as a guide, we learn six lessons.

Lesson 1: Identifying the theories, evidence, priors, and likelihoods that are part of our inference helps us map out potential flaws in our reasoning.

Lesson 2: Using stereotypes and representativeness to reach a conclusion, as we do intuitively, is an invitation to error.

Lesson 3: Neglecting to estimate the prior probability of each theory is a potential source of error. We must account for the probability that each theory is likely to be true before accounting for the evidence.

Lesson 4: We can improve our estimates of priors and likelihoods with a simple online search. We do not have to rely on the brain's poor judgment of probabilities. We can ask a search engine how many Americans wear glasses, how many salespeople there are, and how many librarians there are.

Lesson 5: We do not need to know precise probabilities and likelihoods. Bayesian reasoning is useful when inputting gross estimates. We can be generous with a theory and see if it makes any difference to our conclusion. In our example, we were especially generous to the librarian theory, yet we still concluded that there was only a about a 5% chance that Dave was a librarian. Presumably, more realistic estimates and inputs would make it even less likely Dave is a librarian based on the evidence. Precise and accurate probabilities are only important when inferences cannot be decided based on gross estimates.

Lesson 6: Bayes' theorem tells us what questions to ask to get a better conclusion. For example, if we want to improve this estimate, we should look for research about the relative frequency of introversion by occupation.

All this from a simple formula.

4.4   Medical Testing

Suppose a mammogram has a 90% true positive rate and a 1% false positive rate. That is, if a patient has breast cancer, the test has a 90% probability of giving a positive result (and thus a 10% probability of a false negative result), and if the patient does not have breast cancer, the test has a 1% probability of giving a false positive result (and thus a 99% probability of a true negative). Suppose approximately one in 1,000 women who get tested has breast cancer. Given this information, what is the probability that a patient who receives a positive result on a mammogram has breast cancer?

This question is perhaps the most common example given to students learning Bayesian reasoning. It is a famous example because this question was given to physicians as part of a famous psychological study. Most physicians who participated in the study answered this question incorrectly.[8]

The intuitive answer is that there is close to a 90% chance that the patient has breast cancer. The actual answer is closer to 10%.

To see why, we go back to our formula.

First, we identify our theories and the evidence.

T_A = The patient has breast cancer.

T_B = The patient does not have breast cancer.

E = The mammogram test showed a positive result.

Next, we enter our priors. This is the step that physicians (and our natural intuitions) fail to take. Since only one in 1,000 women has breast cancer, the prior probability that a patient has the disease is extremely low.

---

[8] Eddy, D. (1982). *Probabilistic reasoning in clinical medicine: Problems and opportunities.* In D. Kahneman, P. Slovic, & A. Tversky (Eds.), *Judgment under Uncertainty: Heuristics and Biases* (pp. 249-267). Cambridge: Cambridge University Press. https://doi.org/10.1017/CBO9780511809477.019

$$P(T_A) = 1 \ in \ 1{,}000 = 0.1\%$$

$$P(T_B) = 999 \ in \ 1{,}000 = 99.9\%$$

$$P(T_A|E) = \frac{P(T_A)P(E|T_A)}{P(T_A)P(E|T_A) + P(T_B)P(E|T_B)}$$

$$= \frac{0.1\% \ P(E|T_A)}{0.1\% \ P(E|T_A) + 99.9\% \ P(E|T_B)}$$

Next, we input the likelihoods. We are told that the probability of a positive result given the patient has the disease is 90%, and the probability of a positive result given the patient does not have the disease is 1%:

$$P(E|T_A) = 90\%$$

$$P(E|T_B) = 1\%$$

$$P(T_A|E) = \frac{0.1\% \ P(E|T_A)}{0.1\% \ P(E|T_A) + 99.9\% \ P(E|T_B)}$$

$$= \frac{0.1\% \ 90\%}{0.1\% \ 90\% + 99.9\% \ 1\%}$$

$$= \frac{0.09\%}{0.09\% + 0.99\%}$$

$$= 8.3\%$$

If our test is 90% accurate, why does a positive result yield such a weak conclusion? The answer is that the base rate of breast cancer is so low that the false positives overwhelm the true positives. Essentially, the claim that the patient has breast cancer is an extraordinary one. Our mammogram test is excellent, but a single test does not rise to the level of extraordinary evidence for such an extraordinary claim.

This is easier to picture when we use frequencies instead of probabilities. For every 10 people with the disease who take the test, nine will test positive. Meanwhile, for every 100 people who do not have the disease, one will get a false positive. For every 10,000 people tested, only 10 are expected to actually have the disease, and 9,990 will not. Thus, if 10,000 people take the test, nine out of 10 people with the disease will get true positives, and 99 of healthy patients will receive false positives. That is a total of 108 positive results, only nine of which are true positives.

This relatively low percentage does not mean the test is useless. The probability that a patient has breast cancer has gone from 0.1% before the test to 8.3% after receiving a positive result. This is almost 10 times higher and enough to warrant further investigation. In medical testing, the effectiveness of a test is often limited by the false positive rate. If the false positive rate is too high, patients may undergo needless testing and procedures, as well as incur unnecessary worry.

Again, the Bayesian approach reveals a flaw in our intuition and teaches us to pay careful attention to the base rate that informs our prior probabilities.

4.4.1   Anecdotal Evidence

Many controversies that swirl in public consciousness involve questionable claims of causation. When we make policy regarding the economy, pollution, education, food, medicine, and social activity, we are asserting a cause-and-effect relationship between the policy and the expected outcomes. In high-stakes issues, both sides of the issue will try to woo you to their team by tricking you into making a bad inference.

One of the most powerful tricks used is the anecdote. We love stories and find it easy to identify with named, described individuals. In fact, we are often more moved by one person's tragedy than by tragic injury to many thousands of people. An emotional story in which a named individual wins or loses can win our hearts, but as we know, the anecdote may not be representative of the statistical norm. In many cases, the anecdote is not even an accurate portrayal of the individual incident.

Of course, anecdotes are a form of evidence. If your friend tells you about a recent experience, they are providing you anecdotal evidence that requires an explanation of some kind. However, there are several ways in which the reporting of anecdotes can mislead us. First, our memory is faulty. Memory is not like videotape. When we recall a memory, we are reconstructing a simulation of the past event based on what we presently believe, based on how we think the original scene must have been. When we revise our beliefs, this can alter our memory of the past. Even seemingly vivid memories are subject to this sort of revision. Psychology experiments have shown that it is relatively easy to implant false memories into a subject,[9] and so-called flashbulb memories of important historical events are no more reliable than other types of memory. The best anecdotes are backed up by other kinds of evidence, such as photographs or medical records taken by unbiased third parties.

Second, many anecdotes are secondhand, which can lead to double counting. If two friends tell you they heard of someone who found $10,000 stashed in the back seat of their car, are they both talking about the same person? Or is it an urban legend that has become a false memory?

Finally, we tend to take anecdotes as more representative of typical experience than we ought to. People only share notable anecdotes, neglecting the uninteresting ones. By the time an anecdote reaches your ears, it has passed through a filter that excludes the mundane stories that are more representative of reality. To turn anecdotes into data, we need to verify the authenticity of the anecdote, and then place it into the context of all the mundane events that surround it.

---

[9] Loftus, E.F.; Pickrell JE (1995). *The formation of false memories.* Psychiatric Annals. 25 (12): 720–725. doi:10.3928/0048-5713-19951201-07.

Coincidences happen. Indeed, a world without coincidences would be peculiar.[10] Even where there is no causation, we should expect to find anecdotes that make it appear as if there is a causal connection. In the U.S., the incidence of cancer is about 439 for every 100,000 people. If there are 100,000 users of a commercial product, we can expect about 439 of them to get cancer, all things being equal. If 100 users of a popular product claim the product gave them cancer, that may sound like impressive evidence, but they will have much more work to do before they can convince a rational thinker that the product caused their cancers. Unless they can show that the users of the product develop cancer more than the comparable nonuser, they do not even have the beginnings of a case. Thus, 100 anecdotes are not much better than a single anecdote without a

---

[10] Interestingly, cancers can go into spontaneous remission (i.e., the cancer is eliminated without treatment). Sometimes, the body's immune system learns to recognize the tumor cells as invaders and jumps into action to rid the body of cancer. Sometimes the body's immune system does this after stimulation from an outside infection. Spontaneous remission is rare in diagnosed patients, estimated to be about one to two in every 100,000 cancers. This translates to about 20 or more spontaneous remissions every year in the U.S. alone. This surely makes for some amazing anecdotes. —G. B. Challis & H. J. Stam (1990). *The Spontaneous Regression of Cancer: A review of cases from 1900 to 1987*, Acta Oncologica, 29:5, 545-550, DOI: 10.3109/02841869009090048.

statistical justification that ties them together and relates them to the bigger picture.

In Bayesian terms, we cannot justify a theory based on evidence without showing that P(evidence|alternative) is smaller. There is nothing wrong with anecdotal evidence in general; statistical evidence is often a statistical tabulation of anecdotes. The key is that we can only responsibly use anecdotes when we can validate the stories and craft a Bayesian argument out of them.

4.5   Interpreting Science

If rational inference is Bayesian and we think science is rational, we ought to be able to understand good science in Bayesian terms.

A defining feature of science is controlled experimentation. The goal of a controlled experiment is to look for a signal, the presence of which is due to just one cause, typically an experimental intervention. For example, when measuring the effect of a drug on the life span of mice, scientists control the experiment by eliminating nondrug factors that might alter the life span of the mice. There are many factors that could affect the life spans of a batch of mice in an experiment (e.g., the time of year when the mice are born, the genetic similarity of the mice, the amount of interaction the mice have with the experimenters, the quantity of material consumed by the mice). If experimenters give the drug to every single mouse in their experiment and the mice lived longer than average mice, the experimenters might not know whether the drug had worked or there was an

Applications

alternative explanation. It is possible that the mice in their experiment were born with better than average genes, or the interaction of the experimenters with the mice gave the mice the kind of healthy stimulation that average mice do not receive.

To eliminate alternative explanations for the extended life spans of the mice, scientists run part of the experiment as a control group. The control group is a randomly selected subset of mice from the same batch. They are the same age and are fed and treated in the same way. If the drug is administered by injection, the control group will receive injections of a placebo. That way, the experiences of all the mice will be identical, except that some mice receive the real drug.

In Bayesian terms, our hypothetical experimenters are trying to distinguish between two theories. Theory A is that the drug extends the life of mice, and theory B is that the drug has no effect or reduces the life span of mice. If mice who are given the drug live longer, the evidence, E, is the longer life of the experimental mice.

The experimenters want to know what is the probability that the drug extends the life of mice, given that the mice in the experiment lived longer:

$$P(T_A|E) = \frac{P(T_A)P(E|T_A)}{P(T_A)P(E|T_A) + P(T_B)P(E|T_B)}$$

For simplicity, let's assume for now that the experimenters believed the drug had even odds of extending the life span of the mice. This is equivalent to saying that the prior probabilities of T_A and T_B were both equal to 50%:

$$P(T_A|E) = \frac{50\% \, P(E|T_A)}{50\% \, P(E|T_A) + 50\% \, P(E|T_B)}$$

$$= \frac{P(E|T_A)}{P(E|T_A) + P(E|T_B)}$$

With this simplification, we see that the result of the experiment comes down to the relative likelihoods of mice living longer with the drug versus without. To make the experiment conclusive, $P(E|T_B)$ must be minimized. If we could reduce $P(E|T_B)$ to zero, then $P(T_A|E)$ would approach unity, and we would know that T_A is correct.

Thus, scientists aim to minimize $P(E|T_B)$ by considering as many possible causes of false positives in an experiment. This is scientific control—ensuring that scientific tests are as conclusive as possible.

To put it in more general terms, we can think of our formula as expressing a ratio between the probability of seeing the evidence if our theory is true and the total probability number of expected events in all theories:

posterior probability

$$= \frac{\textit{probability of E given our theory}}{\textit{probability of E given our theory} + \textit{probability of E given alternatives}}$$

Per common sense, the more probable it is that we could see the evidence if our theory were not true, the less the evidence will inspire confidence in our theory. The goal of scientific control is to minimize the second term in the denominator and make the evidence more conclusive for our theory.

4.6   Evolutionary Biology

Why is evolutionary biology the most rational explanation for life on Earth? Most people who examine the evidence for evolutionary biology find the evidence from genetics and the fossil record to be the most persuasive. Yet, when those persuaded are asked precisely why the evidence is so compelling, it can be difficult for them to give a concise answer. Using the Bayesian approach, the answer is straightforward.

The theory of evolutionary biology is based on a few simple principles. Life forms reproduce, preserving most of their traits, but there is some variation from one generation to the next. This variation may be the result of blending the traits of parents that reproduce sexually, or it may be a kind of random genetic mutation (due to radiation, viral infection, or some other cause). Some individuals are better suited to their environment than their peers, so they go on to survive and reproduce better than their competitors. This process of variation and natural selection leads to the multitude of species that we see today. The process takes a long time because adaptations are only proven generation by generation. Though this blind, natural process, biology can, in principle, create all the species we see today. The theory makes sense of a fossil record in which we see species in one era borrow the basic design of species in the era that came millions of years before.

Charles Darwin did not know about DNA molecules, but molecular genetics tells us that we share 99.9% of our DNA with our fellow humans, 96% with chimpanzees, 90% with cats,[11] and 60% with bananas. All life on Earth is related, and the degree of similarity of our genetic codes corresponds with the closeness of our nearest common ancestor.

Still, some critics argue that this similarity does not rule out intelligent design. They point to gaps in our knowledge of evolutionary history and argue that evolutionary biology should not be accepted until we can explain every step of our evolutionary journey. Indeed, we can easily imagine an ingenious designer tinkering with the genetic codes of life on Earth to bring about human life as we see it today. What is wrong with these design arguments?

Let's go back to Six-Twenty. If evolutionary biology is the rational inference, it must be because evolutionary biology is analogous to D6, while design is analogous to D20. Indeed, this is the case. Just like D6, evolutionary biology is a more restrictive theory. Evolutionary biology predicts that life will proceed from one generation to the next with descent by reproduction. Each life form is

---

[11] Pontius, Joan & Mullikin, James & Smith, Douglas & Lindblad-Toh, Kerstin & Gnerre, Sante & Clamp, Michele & Chang, Jean & Stephens, Robert & Neelam, Beena & Volfovsky, Natalia & Schaffer, Alejandro & Agarwala, Richa & Narfström, Kristina & Murphy, William & Giger, Urs & Roca, Alfred & Antunes, Agostinho & Menotti-Raymond, Marilyn & Yuhki, Naoya & O'Brien, Stephen. (2007). *Initial sequence and comparative analysis of the cat genome.* Genome research. 17. 1675-89. https://doi.org/10.1101/gr.6380007.

descended by birth from a parent or parents. Design, in contrast, makes no such prediction. For example, automobiles are not created through reproduction. No car has ever been born to another car. Instead, we designers use factories. Of course, we might one day devise cars that give birth to cars, but, as designers, we are not limited to breeding cars.

As a corollary to descent, evolutionary biology also predicts common descent. That is, every individual on Earth is related to a common ancestor (or perhaps a small number of common ancestors). Finally, we are all made from the same stuff. All animal cells use the same basic mechanisms for reproducing and transporting energy throughout their cells. We all have genetic codes written in DNA, and the cells of all plants and animals are built out of similar lipid (fat) layers. In designed engineering, there is no such restriction that forces us to use the same technologies or materials. We can swap a gasoline engine for a battery and electric motor or replace wood construction with metals. Evolutionary biology innovates, but it cannot replace materials or complex components wholesale.

Thus, evolutionary biology is heavily constrained by its blind mechanisms and can only create certain kinds of ecosystems over millions of years. Design, in contrast, can create wholly unrelated species, use manufacturing instead of descent, and employ completely different materials and mechanisms for each form of life. Even with our limited human imagination, we can think of trillions of things a designer could create which are beyond the ability of evolution.

Imagine nuclear-powered elephants, plastic turtles, and vampires that are invulnerable to physical attack.

If evolutionary biology is analogous to a six-sided die, then design is analogous to a die with many more sides. How many? That is difficult to say, but it probably has many more sides. To see why this is, consider that for each species we observe to be constrained by biological evolution, an omnipotent designer could have created something radically different in composition, size, behavior, intelligence, complexity, and ability. Whether this means dice representing design have 20 sides or 20,000 sides makes little difference to our conclusion. We have many thousands of observations in the fossil record and in the biochemical similarity of different species and have never seen anything inconsistent with evolutionary biology. This is like playing Six-Twenty many thousands of times and always seeing rolls between one and six.

What about gaps in the fossil record?

Evolutionary biology has been established by thousands of pieces of evidence, and it would take extraordinary evidence to tip the scales back. It is not a prediction of the theory that there will be no gaps in the fossil record. Nor does the theory predict that we will be able to reconstruct the evolutionary history of life on Earth at the molecular level. Indeed, even if a researcher came forward with the claim that a species was not a participant in common descent, it would be an extraordinary claim requiring extraordinary evidence.

One of the biggest gaps in our knowledge of evolutionary history is the origin of life itself. There are several theories that posit explanations for how life began on Earth, but none of these theories have made enough testable predictions to gain a decisive advantage over its competitors. Nonetheless, based on what we have already inferred, we know with extreme confidence that life evolved through natural means, even if the detailed mechanism is yet unknown.

To see why, imagine you are on a jury deciding the guilt of a defendant accused of burglary. The court presents CCTV video evidence of the defendant at the scene on the night of the burglary. The defendant's fingerprints are on the safe, and the stolen goods were discovered at the defendant's home. This seems like an open-and-shut case. However, the defense argues that the prosecution cannot explain how the defendant traveled from his home to the scene of the crime. The defendant has no car, and local bus drivers do not recall seeing the defendant on the bus that night. Obviously, this defense is not enough to convince you the defendant is innocent. There is already overwhelming evidence that the defendant committed the crime, and gaps in your knowledge about the crime are not the kinds of extraordinary evidence required to swing the verdict. Similarly, through Bayesian updating, we now have near-certain confidence in blind evolutionary processes. There are still mysteries to be solved, but the gaps in our knowledge do not threaten that confidence.

4.7   Fine-Tuning

In the previous section, I explained why unguided evolution wins the Bayesian inference battle against intelligent design. However, it is natural to ask whether we can narrow our generic theory of intelligent design to make it more competitive. Suppose we devise a narrower theory in which the designer insists on using seemingly unguided evolution to create life. Perhaps the designer created the initial conditions, knowing that without further input, humanity would come to exist as it does today. Or perhaps the designer has intervened in the evolutionary process in ways too subtle for us to detect. By fine-tuning the generic theory of intelligent design into this narrow design theory, we can construct a theory that has equal Bayesian likelihood probabilities as blind evolutionary theory. This narrow design theory predicts descent, common descent, and common composition, just like blind evolution does. Can this maneuver save the design theory?

Fine-tuning comes at a cost. Unless it allows much better predictions to be made, fine-tuning does not allow a losing theory to keep up. To see why, we need to look at the prior probabilities.

Although we may talk about a theory as if it is a single thing, a theory is more like a set or category of deeper, more specific theories. To explain this, I will use a simpler example. Suppose you and your co-workers are theorizing about how another co-worker, Dave, traveled to work this morning, and you begin with two theories: Dave took public transport to work or Dave traveled by personal means, such as bicycle or car. Assuming Dave successfully traveled to work this morning, the prior probabilities of these two theories must add up to 100% (Dave got to work somehow):

$$P(arrival) = P(public\ transport) + P(personal)$$

$$= 100\%$$

The theory that Dave took public transport to work today includes all public transport possibilities, including the possibilities that he took a bus, he took a train, and he took a combination of the two. Each of these more specific possibilities is a more specific theory than the generic public transport theory. In most cases, you could keep dividing your theories into ever more specific theories. For example, the theory that Dave took the train to work includes the possibilities that Dave took the 8:00 a.m. train, the 9:00 a.m. train, etc.

Whenever we assign a prior probability to a theory, we implicitly assign each subset of the theory a portion of the total prior probability. Thus, if you estimate that the prior probability that Dave took public transport to work today is 66%, then the prior probability that Dave relied exclusively on a bus must be less than 66%. Indeed, assuming it is equally likely Dave took a train, bus, or combination of the two, the prior probability that he relied on any one of the three methods is 22%:

$$P(public\ transport) = 66\%$$

$$= P(bus) + P(train) + P(bus + train)$$

$$= 22\% + 22\% + 22\%$$

Of course, if the prior P(public transport) = 66%, then P(personal) = 34%, so that the probabilities total 100%.

Consider what happens if you receive evidence that Dave did not take public transport. Suppose you know that Dave showed up to work on time, but you also know that there were long train delays this morning. This new information should make you think that it is more likely Dave that did not take public transport to work this morning. This is because, of all the public transport routes Dave could have taken, two-thirds of them involved trains and would likely have delayed his arrival at the office. Meanwhile, if Dave drove his car to work, there is no reason to think he would have been delayed. We just use Bayes' theorem:

$P(public\ transport|E)$

$$= \frac{P(public\ transport)P(E|public\ transport)}{P(public\ transport)P(E|public\ transport) + P(personal)P(E|personal)}$$

where E is the new evidence about Dave's timely arrival during the train delays. Because the public transport theory contains three different theories, the numerator is made up of three terms corresponding to the three more specific theories:

$P(public\ transport)P(E|public\ transport)$

$$= P(bus)P(E|bus) + P(train)P(E|train)$$

$$+ P(bus + train)P(E|bus + train)$$

Since any method of transport that includes a train ride would make Dave late to work, their likelihoods are zero. All other methods of travel will allow Dave to reach work on time:

$$P(E|train) = 0\%$$

$$P(E|bus + train) = 0\%$$

$$P(E|bus) = 100\%$$

$$P(E|personal) = 100\%$$

Taking these into account, our posterior probability looks like this:

$$P(public\ transport|E) = \frac{P(bus)P(E|bus)}{P(bus)P(E|bus) + P(personal)P(E|personal)}$$

$$= \frac{22\%\ 100\%}{22\%\ 100\% + 34\%\ 100\%}$$

$$= 39\%$$

The evidence that Dave arrived on time during a train delay should cause you to revise your confidence in the public transport theory from 66% down to 39%. So far, this is standard Bayesian reasoning.

Fine-tuning is what happens when we redefine a broad theory by identifying it with a narrower theory it contains. In our commuter example, fine-tuning occurs when we identify the public transport theory with the bus theory. Because you now know that Dave did not take a train, you might catch yourself saying, "The public transport theory is the theory that Dave took the bus to work this morning."

In general, there is nothing wrong with fine-tuning, as long as we keep track of our priors. Indeed, every great theory has been fine-tuned to match observations. The predictive power of a good theory—the power of a fine-tuned theory's likelihood to make predictions that outperform alternative theories—is what keeps a fine-tuned theory competitive. However, fine-tuning becomes irrational when priors are neglected and likelihoods do not outperform the competition.

In the example of Dave's transportation to work, you would be irrational if you fine-tuned the public transport theory to identify it with a bus ride and kept the prior probability at 66% instead of reducing it to 22%. If you fine-tune without shrinking your prior probability accordingly, the evidence that trains were running late would have no effect on your estimate, and you would still have a 66% posterior confidence in the public transport theory instead of a 39% confidence.

We can now return to our discussion of intelligent design and see how its fine-tuning is irrational. The original intelligent design theory—the theory to which we might have granted 50% prior—could produce any imaginable world without restriction. Indeed, generic intelligent design makes no predictions at all. The fine-tuned theory of intelligent design has been drastically narrowed to be capable of producing only the same kinds of worlds that blind evolutionary biology can create. This represents an infinitesimal sliver of the possible worlds that generic design can create, and so it ought to receive a correspondingly tiny slice of the prior probability we would initially have granted to intelligent design.

To sum up, fine-tuning can always occur, but the price for fine-tuning is that the prior for a fine-tuned theory is smaller. However, a fine-tuned theory can pay off this debt by making predictions that are better than its competitors.

4.8 Scientific Failures

The media reports on many scientific studies each week. Many of these studies will fail to be replicated or will be contradicted by future research. What is going on?

Science experiments fail either because of bad luck or because they have insufficient control. To put it another way, the experimenters either failed to be Bayesian or they succeeded in being Bayesian but got unlucky.

Luck plays a role because Bayesians can be rational yet arrive at the wrong answer. The output of Bayesian reasoning is a probability estimate. If we shuffle a deck of cards and bet that the top card is not the queen of hearts, we are making a rational wager. We have a 51 in 52 chance of being correct. Yet, we can still lose. Similarly, experiments update our confidence in their conclusion. If an experiment is well-designed and we update our confidence in a theory to 99%, there is still a 1% chance that our confidence is misplaced.

Though luck can be a factor, most science experiments fail because they are weakly controlled. Recall that control is about minimizing the number of ways of getting a positive test result when the correct answer is negative. This can happen in a multitude of ways. To be rational, we must be able to read about studies in the press and make a reasonably skeptical judgment about the scientific conclusion. This is exactly what you will learn on the following pages.

Let's consider a hypothetical experiment and media report that claims a certain blueberry extract supplement is an effective weight loss drug. The report tells us that most of the subjects in the study lost weight. The experiment monitored 10 participants, each of whom was asked to take the drug once per day.

If such a hypothetical story were published, millions of people would likely buy extra blueberries in the hopes of losing weight. But how much confidence should we place in the study?

Before we answer this question, let's address that inevitable public rush to buy blueberries that would result from such a study. Even if the study's conclusion turned out to be accurate, there is a big difference between a blueberry and blueberry extract. For all we know, it takes 1,000 berries to produce enough extract for one pill. Moreover, we can reasonably assume that the extract the researchers tested did not include the fattening fructose and carbohydrates of the complete blueberry. Eating more whole blueberries is probably going to do what we expect it would do: cause people to gain weight rather than lose. We often have difficulty extrapolating from the conclusions of a study—especially where diet and medicine are concerned—because we like to childishly equate a food with the compounds it contains and vice versa.

As for the quality and reliability of the study, we need to dive into the details of how the study was conducted; but even in what little has been described so far, there are already some red flags. The first red flag is that there were only 10 participants in the study. There is a lot of variation from one person to the next, not only in lifestyle, but also in genetics, diet, sleep habits, stress levels, etc. There is also a lot of variation in the behavior and health of each individual. In other words, 10 people is not a large enough sample to determine how the drug would affect the average person.

The second red flag is that there was no control group. Perhaps most people lose weight during the time when the study was conducted, whether they take the drug or not. This might happen if the study began on January 2 and ran for a month (i.e., when most people work to lose weight that they gained over the holiday season). To isolate the effects of the drug from other common factors, experimenters typically enroll a control group consisting of people who will not take the drug, using the control group as a reference point. These two red flags are enough for us to immediately conclude that the results of the study should not be used to update our expectations by very much.

Suppose we find the original academic paper describing the study. The paper tells us that the participants in the study weighed themselves at the start of the two-month trial and at its conclusion. The researchers were looking for a positive result in the form of participants weighing less at the end of the study than at the beginning. As Bayesians, we ask ourselves, "How might it be possible for the reported weights of the participants to drop over the course of the study if the drug in fact does not work?"

There are many possibilities, for example:

- The participants might have been unusually heavier at the start of the study.
- The participants may have weighed themselves at irregular times of the day.
- The participants used their own scales, which may not be accurate or precise over time.
- The participants' weight fluctuates naturally, and they happened to weigh less at the end of the study.
- Some participants may have become ill during the study.
- The participants may not have been taking the drug as ordered.
- The participants may have lied about their weight.
- Some of the participants may have altered their exercise regimen or diet during the study.
- Taking the pill may have caused participants to alter their daily routine in subtle ways, such as eating at different times during the day or consuming more water.

All of these factors could cause some participants in the study to end up weighing less at the end than at the start, whether the drug works or not. Even if the pills did work, all of these factors might mask the drug's success by causing the participants to gain more weight by external factors than they lost because of the drug. Thus, the signal the researchers were hoping to see—that people lost weight on the drug—may be drowned out by the noise of weight gain or loss from all the other factors.

Controlling a study is an attempt to limit noise and prevent external factors from interfering with the test. Controls could be explicit attempts to eliminate factors, such as weighing all the participants on the same, well-calibrated scale, administering the drug directly, or asking participants not to change their exercise or diet regimen during the study. However, controls may also be statistical in nature. If a study has many participants and the participants are divided into an intervention group and a control group, experimenters can hope that random factors cancel themselves out. For example, in a large, randomized study, as many people will recover from an illness as will succumb to it, and as many people will be in natural weight gain cycles as in will be in weight loss cycles. If averages drift during the study, statistically, the control group average will move in the same way as the intervention group. Using the control group as a reference can help us see through the noise in the data.

4.9   P-Hacking

Science can appear to be statistically responsible while failing to be Bayesian. A common measure of effectiveness in scientific papers is called the *p-value*. The p-value is intended to measure the significance of a scientific result. If there is only a 5% chance that an experimental observation could have been caused by random chance, the observation is said to have a p-value of 0.05 and therefore scientifically interesting.

The formal definition of p-value is quite sophisticated, and the definition assumes we understand the random statistics that might potentially throw off our results. To see how this works, we will use an oversimplified example: our game of Six-Twenty.

Recall that in Six-Twenty, we begin at a point of ignorance about which of the dice, the six-sided or 20-sided die, was selected. After the first round in which a die falls in the range of one to six, we computed that there was about a 77% chance that we were dealing with the six-sided die. After a second roll of the die falls in the range of one to six, our confidence in the six-sided die theory rises to 91%. And after the third roll of the die falls in the range of one to six, there is a 97% chance that the six-sided die was selected. Thus, after three rolls of the die, the probability that we got unlucky and the 20-sided die was chosen is only 3%. This is equivalent to a p-value of 0.03—and is a measure of how powerful our inference is from playing three rounds of the game. According to the p-value standard, our Six-Twenty game is quite good at discerning between the two dice after only three rounds.

In many cases, the p-value is a good measure of significance. However, there are cases where the p-value is misleading or the p-value standard has been abused.

The main problem with the p-value standard is that it is a function of likelihoods but not priors. In Six-Twenty, we calculate the p-value as follows:

$$pvalue = \frac{P(E_N|T_B)}{P(E_N|T_A) + P(E_N|T_B)}$$

where T_A is the six-sided die theory, T_B is the 20-sided die theory, and E_N is the evidence of playing N rounds of the game and observing a roll of one to six in every round. Whenever we play N rounds of the game, the calculated p-value tells us the power of the inference we can make from those N rounds taken in isolation.

However, because the p-value does not depend on our priors, the p-value alone cannot be used to infer the significance of an experiment where the priors are strongly in favor of one of the theories. Suppose we begin a new game of Six-Twenty, but we will divide our game into two experiments with two experimenters. Alice, our first experimenter, observes the first roll of the die to be 17. Satisfied that the 20-sided die was selected, Alice concludes her part of the game and writes down her conclusion in her notebook. (For argument's sake, let's suppose Alice's p-value is 0.000001.)

Our second experimenter, Bob, enters the room and continues the same game with the same die. Bob plays three rounds of the game, and in these next three rounds, each roll of the die is consistent with the six-sided die. As we calculated above, these three rounds have a p-value of 0.03, so Bob concludes there is only a 3% chance of seeing such a result if the 20-sided die was selected. Bob makes a note of his results and his p-value and concludes his experiment.

As independent observers, both Alice and Bob have made rational conclusions. However, if Alice and Bob share their notes and combine their information into a single experiment, Bob ought to alter his opinion and agree with Alice.

Alas, scientists in the real world are under pressure to publish their work in journals and gain prestige and press for their respective institutions. This means Alice wants to publish her paper and Bob wants to publish his. Each is vying for attention and esteem. Though Alice has all but settled the issue, Bob wants to publish his paper. If having a p-value less that 0.05 is the only standard of significance required for a scientist to publish his result, Bob can accurately say he has done a good experiment and concluded that the six-sided die was in play. Of course, this makes little sense. Bob's conclusion is a good one only by ignoring the fact that Alice has already set a very low prior with her initial experiment.

P-values are reasonable measures of inferential power when priors are 50/50. But once a conclusion has been well-established, p-values of 0.05 are only enough to dislodge priors of comparable magnitude. Scientists, journal editors, and their referees must be wary of p-value as an exclusive arbiter of a scientific result.

P-values have been so prized that some scientists have repeated failed experiments until they obtained a result with a p-value low enough for publication. This technique is known as p-hacking. Whenever some amount of randomness is involved (most cases), a careless or nefarious researcher can repeat an experiment until, by chance, they get the desired result. In our example, if Bob wants to see the six-sided die with a p-value of 0.05, he can just keep looking at rolls of the die, terminating an experimental run when the roll is greater than a six. Eventually, Bob will hit on a streak of three rolls in which each roll is six or less. About one in 30 experiments will give Bob the answer he is looking, for with a p-value that will get him published.

As we learned, extraordinary claims require extraordinary evidence. Once a conclusion is well-established, we require extraordinarily good evidence before we can overturn it. A well-established theory cannot be displaced by an experiment with a good p-value. It can only be displaced by an experiment with an extraordinary p-value. A good p-value is not enough when a theory is well-established.

There are numerous ways that experimentalists can hack their results to make them appear statistically significant. A 2011 paper in *Psychological Science*[12] described ways researchers could employ legitimate statistical analyses and truthful reporting yet use ambiguity in research protocols to arrive at misleading conclusions. For example, experimenters have flexibility in choosing when to switch from exploration to testing and when to declare an end to data collection. They also have flexibility in choosing how much of their data they will report.

---

[12] Simmons, Joseph & Nelson, Leif & Simonsohn, Uri. (2011). *False-positive psychology: Undisclosed flexibility in data collection and analysis allows presenting anything as significant.* Psychological Science. 20. 1-8. 10.5334/jopd.aa.

For example, suppose we are measuring consumer preference for a type of automobile. We get to decide how to classify vehicles as trucks, sport utility vehicles, hatchbacks, and sedans. We then can collect data on several variables, such as gender, age range, income, geographic location, number of children, religious background, and marital status. If each of these seven variables has three to four different classifications, there are between 6,500–65,000 unique classifications across all the variables. Even if we collected detailed interviews from 1,000 consumers (a huge undertaking), we would still end up with a sparse amount of data in each unique classification. If we are looking for patterns, we will need to ignore some of our data dimensions and pool data in single classifications or pairs of classifications, such as how does choice of vehicle correlate with religious background, or how does choice of vehicle correlate with both income and marital status.

Since we have seven simple correlations to examine and 21 pair correlations to look at, our single experiment now looks like 28 different experiments. If our p-value standard is only 0.05 (one in 20 experiments is a false positive) and we implicitly have more than 20 experiments, it would not be surprising if at least one of our correlations turns out to be a false positive. If we publish our paper on the positive result and fail to notice or disclose our procedural mistakes, we can easily mislead the community (and the media) with false positives.

4.10 Supernatural Versus Superstition

Rational inference encompasses science, but it applies even to those things not normally considered scientific. As Bayesians, the only thing we require of a rationally comprehensible world is predictability. Any theory that makes predictions that we can convert into differential likelihoods is a candidate for our methods of justification. These likelihoods need not be precise, but once we have them, we have a basis for interpreting evidence. Of course, just as scientists do, we need to be aware of alternative theories that would generate false positives.

The term *supernatural* most commonly refers to a phenomenon outside the processes normally described by sciences (i.e., outside of physics and chemistry). Though the supernatural stands outside of physics, in principle, a supernatural theory could still make predictions. In other words, assuming the necessary evidence exists, a rational person could be convinced that a supernatural theory is correct.

One of the principles of inductive inference is that extraordinary claims require extraordinary evidence. If supernatural magic were commonplace, supernatural theories would not be extraordinary and would not need extraordinary evidence. For example, in the fictional world of Harry Potter, wizards and witches perform magical tasks reliably and as a matter of course. In Harry Potter's world, magical laws are not much different than physical laws, and experiments can be performed to show that magical laws exist and are reliable.

While the word "supernatural" signifies an alternative kind of causation, the term *superstition* connotes an alternative kind of epistemology: irrational epistemology. A superstitious belief is a belief that one arrives at by ignoring rational considerations such as logical consistency, likelihoods, false positives, and priors.

For example, astrology is the idea that the relative positions of the stars and planets determine our personalities or determine what events are more likely to occur in our lives at any given time. The conditions present during formative periods of our childhood can have an impact on our personalities, so it is at least plausible that people born at a certain time of year might have an above average number of traits in common. Astrologists assert that the present positions of celestial objects affect our fortunes in such as way that violates the laws of physics. This is a supernatural claim. As we explained, there is nothing wrong with a supernatural theory so long as the theory makes predictions.

Unfortunately for astrologers, their predictions have been scientifically tested and have been found not to work. Why is it then that so many people believe in astrology?

The short answer is that believers in astrology are not being good Bayesians. To become a believer in astrology, a Bayesian would look for well-controlled tests of astrological predictions and demand that these tests are strong enough to overcome low priors and alternative explanations for the evidence. A person who truly wants to know if astrology is real would ask questions like a Bayesian: What precisely do the horoscopes predict, and how can we test the predictions with an experiment? If a horoscope were accurate, what would be measurably different? If a horoscope were no better than fiction, what other effects might cause me to mistakenly think it was accurate?

The average believer in astrology asks different questions: Is there any *possible* way my traits align with those ascribed to my astrological sign? If I make a choice in accordance with the horoscope, is there any *possible* way I can interpret the consequences as right for me?

The traits ascribed to the astrological signs are so general that almost everyone would count them as accurate, if they are interpreted conveniently. For example, horoscope.com states, "Virgo has a rich inner life and can sometimes seem shy at first meeting. A Virgo won't spill secrets right away, and it's important to earn a Virgo's trust." This is true of many people, Virgo or not.

"An Aries will always tell you what they're thinking, with a frankness that may occasionally border on rudeness." Again, this is simultaneously true of many people, depending on how broadly it is interpreted.

Indeed, if you write a general personality description and tell people it was drawn up based on their personal criteria, people will generally agree that it is an accurate description of their own personality. This is known as the Barnum effect—the technical name for the phenomenon that people generally overrate the accuracy and specificity of general personality descriptions.[13]

A Bayesian would think about astrology by considering all the terms in the formula for posterior probability. First, are my priors suitably small, given what we know about physics? Second, what precise prediction is being made by the horoscope? For example, since horoscopes are different for people born in different parts of the year, we ought to be able to predict a person's birthday based on their personality profile.

This sort of experiment has been performed, and of course, astrologers fail the test.[14] The failure to pass the test has nothing to do with the fact that they allege a supernatural effect. They fail because their model either fails to make a testable prediction or because mundane alternatives are more likely.

Thus, belief in astrology is a kind of superstition—an irrational, non-Bayesian belief derived from a failure to ask pertinent questions and carefully consider the evidence.

---

[13] Also known as the Forer effect, the Barnum effect was so named in reference to the P.T. Barnum quote, "We've got something for everyone."

[14] Carlson, Shawn. (1985). *A double-blind test of astrology.* Nature. 318. 419-425. 10.1038/318419a0.

4.11   Pseudoscience

Pseudoscience is a class of endeavor that superficially resembles a scientific discipline but which fails to be truly scientific or rational. Pseudoscientific fields are created or led by people with diehard beliefs in phenomena or principles that contradict well-tested scientific results or, at least, lie outside of what is scientifically verifiable.

Pseudoscience sometimes begins in the laboratory. An experiment teases a profound new possibility, and laypeople are inspired to hope and believe. This brings true believers into labs around the world, and despite setbacks, they persist in their research for years on end.

When a field of scientific research is new, our instrumentation is often primitive or operating at its limits. We are likely to have only a small number of data points, and we may not know what questions to ask or what experiments will be the most revealing. Under these circumstances, we can expect early studies to have weakly supported conclusions. False positives are to be expected. As the field progresses, more researchers get involved, more data is collected, and new controls are devised. If the initial results are true positives, we expect a predictive theory to emerge and successive experiments to reliably replicate earlier ones. As the field progresses, scientists not only know that an effect is real, they also learn how the effect works and learn to make novel predictions verified by future experiments.

On the other hand, if early experiments present us with false positives, we expect that future experiments will fail to replicate the result reliably. Future experiments may produce more false positives, providing fodder for the media, but conclusive evidence will elude us. The nascent science fails to get off the ground and is constantly burdened by the task of proving that the effect exists at all. Such scenarios are a breeding ground for pseudoscience, especially when a true result has profound implications for dearly held beliefs about religion, politics, or the future of humanity.

Wouldn't it be wonderful if we could harness psychic powers, reach into past lives, discover that aliens visited the Earth in the past, cure all disease, or access vast amounts of free energy? These are ideas that inspire devotion, and when mainstream researchers fail to reproduce false positive results, the devoted will often accuse the mainstream community of conspiracy, just so they can maintain their beliefs in the face of evidence to the contrary.

Several indicators should make us suspect a field of research is a pseudoscience rather than a legitimate scientific endeavor. Not all the indicators by themselves are conclusively determinative in all cases.

4.11.1   Lack of Progress

As we just discussed, in a field that makes no progress despite years of research, it is more likely that the few successes that have been reported were statistical flukes.

4.11.2   Scientific Consensus

If the majority of scientists believe the field is going nowhere, we should take note, but it may simply mean that the field is on the bleeding edge of innovation. However, if the scientific consensus is that the field is nonsense or physically impossible, there is a high probability that the field is a pseudoscience.

4.11.3   Failure to Publish

A failure to publish in mainstream journals is a sign that the field's researchers cannot muster experiments of high quality, or there are so few scientists who credit the field that no peer reviewers can be found.

4.11.4   Accusations of Conspiracy

If a field of study claims it has failed to persuade the scientific community because of a conspiracy between scientists and government or industry, the field is probably a pseudoscience trying to cover for its scientific shortcomings. Scientific inquiry is vulnerable to funding biases and groupthink, but there is enough variation between funding sources and independence between institutions around the world that science cannot be held back by secret government or industry plots.

4.11.5   Failure to Use Controlled Experiments

Pseudoscience is often used to prop up alternative medical treatments. The challenge with any medical treatment is isolating the effectiveness of the medicine from the patient's expectations or the doctor's bedside manner. A patient's feelings and beliefs can have a profound effect on their perceptions and on the symptoms they report. This effect is driven by psychology, but it has a real physiological effect. The feeling that one is being cared for has an impact on stress hormones and immune response. [15] This is known as the *placebo effect*. For example, giving a patient a fake pain reliever can be somewhat effective at relieving their discomfort. In fact, in one review [16] of nonsteroidal anti-inflammatory drugs, placebo was found to reduce pain by 50% in 18% of subjects, which is about 30% of the pain-relieving effectiveness of ibuprofen by that benchmark.

To eliminate this effect from their assessments, investigators must use double-blind, randomly controlled trials (RCTs). Patients must be selected at random and randomly assigned either to the intervention group or the control group. The intervention group receives the real drug while the control group receives a

---

[15] Price, Donald & Finniss, Damien & Benedetti, Fabrizio. (2008). *A Comprehensive Review of the Placebo Effect: Recent Advances and Current Thought.* Annual review of psychology. 59. 565-90. 10.1146/annurev.psych.59.113006.095941.

[16] Ong, Cliff & Lirk, P & Tan, C.H. & Seymour, Robin. (2007). *An Evidence-Based Update on Nonsteroidal Anti-Inflammatory Drugs.* Clinical medicine & research. 5. 19-34. 10.3121/cmr.2007.698.

placebo. In a blind study, the patients do not know whether they are in the control group or the intervention group. In a double-blind study, even the doctors and researchers do not know which patients are in which group. This means all patients should receive approximately the same care, as far as they can tell, and all should have approximately the same placebo effect, on average. Only at the conclusion of the study can researchers identify which patients received the real drug and which did not. Of course, even RCTs are vulnerable to statistical error. Every doctor-patient interaction is slightly different, and every patient may have different sensitivity to placebos.

There is nothing wrong with leveraging the placebo effect to aid a patient. If the patient's ailment is related to stress or subjective judgment, administering an otherwise ineffective treatment can make a real difference to a patient's sense of well-being. However, the health claims made for pseudoscientific medical practices go far beyond the placebo effect. The placebo effect cannot cure cancers and infections, for example. Any therapy that claims it can cure such diseases has to perform better than placebo.

Often, journal articles on alternative medicine report on the degree to which physicians or patients receive a treatment and report the feedback patients give about the therapy. Alas, testimonials from patients are not a substitute for RCTs. In general, therapies in alternative medicine remain outside the mainstream because they fail to consistently prove their value in RCTs.

4.11.6   Homeopathy

Let's look at an example of a pseudoscience. Homeopathic medicine is premised on the idea that water molecules (H_2O) are not the simple objects that mainstream chemistry believes them to be. Instead, homeopaths believe water retains a memory of the compounds it has interacted with. Moreover, they believe water has complex curative properties. For example, pure water that "remembers" its contact with snake venom is a potent antivenom, they claim. Similarly, exposing water to a pathogen, then diluting the water to the point that not even one molecule of the pathogen remains, turns the diluted water into the cure for the pathogen.

Any student of high school chemistry knows that the homeopath's story contradicts what we know about chemistry and physics. Homeopathy is rejected not only by chemists and physicists but also by mainstream physicians. According to chemistry, diluting water to the point that no molecules of the original foreign compound remain will leave you with nothing but pure water.

Nevertheless, homeopathy is big business, especially in the U.S., where laws permit pharmacies to sell supplements that have no proven efficacy. There are plenty of alternative medicine practitioners willing to sell homeopathic remedies or fund research. In 2005, *The Lancet* published a meta-study by mainstream researchers which looked at 110 prior controlled studies of homeopathic remedies and their counterparts in conventional medicine.[17] They found that the effects of homeopathy were consistent with placebo bias:

Biases are present in placebo-controlled trials of both homoeopathy and conventional medicine. When account was taken for these biases in the analysis, there was weak evidence for a specific effect of homoeopathic remedies, but strong evidence for specific effects of conventional interventions. This finding is compatible with the notion that the clinical effects of homoeopathy are placebo effects.

Other meta-studies end up at similar conclusions. This is typical of a pseudoscience. Instead of a clear consensus emerging that homeopathic treatments are effective, the evidence fails to accumulate. After we factor in placebo biases, publication bias (i.e., the tendency of homeopathy advocates to publish only successful studies) and the fact that homeopathy contradicts other established sciences, there is no effect to speak of.

Compare homeopathy to conventional drug design. Drug designers use the known chemical and biological effects of compounds to intentionally design new

---

[17] Linde, K; Clausius, N; Ramirez, G; Melchart, D; Eitel, F; Hedges, L; Jonas, W (1997). *Are the clinical effects of homoeopathy placebo effects? A meta-analysis of placebo-controlled trials.* The Lancet. 350 (9081): 834–43. doi:10.1016/S0140-6736(97)02293-9.

drugs, and every year, the science of creating new drugs gets better and better. Drug design and chemistry are complementary. The field of conventional drug therapy advances every year, building on the research of prior years. Of course, drug design is difficult. Many drug development projects fail to come to fruition, and many drugs either have low efficacy or have problematic side effects. Yet some drugs are effective and reliable.

In contrast, homeopathic remedies are traditions based on recipes from the last century. Knowledge of the mechanism of homeopathy never accumulates because it contradicts modern chemistry, and no one has a qualitative or quantitative model of what homeopathic remedies do. Had homeopathy been real, we would have seen the emergence of a whole new field of chemistry that is the basis for homeopathic function.

5   HUMAN THINKING

5.1   Bayesian Reasoning and Human Irrationality

In Chapter 3, I described Bayesian reasoning, a plausible candidate for ideal rational inference. In Chapter 4, I demonstrated ways we can use the Bayesian approach to solve problems, or at least understand how to reason about them. We can think of Bayes' theorem as a map that tells us all the factors we need to think about while making an inductive inference. We can use the formula to understand why science works and what scientists are trying to do with their experiments.

Since Bayesian reasoning is a universal method, every correct inference from evidence should be explicable in a Bayesian terms. As we saw in section 4.6, most people intuitively infer that unguided evolution is the best explanation for life on Earth. Yet not everyone reaches the same conclusion intuitively, and even scientists have difficulty explaining precisely why evolution is the best rational explanation. With Bayesian reasoning, we can succinctly explain why the evolutionary explanation is rational.

Bayesian reasoning gives us an *epistemology*—a universal explanation of how we know what we know, how our degrees of confidence are justified, and how we learn new things from evidence. This universality is elegant and powerful. Without a consistent epistemology, we employ wildly different criteria for making inferences in different contexts without a second thought. Having a consistent epistemology is not only about having that second thought but having a specific idea what those second thoughts should be. Do I have the right priors? What are the likelihoods of seeing this evidence? What alternative theories could result in these same observations?

Bayesian reasoning helps us think about degrees of confidence instead of thinking in certainties or hard dichotomies. It helps us think statistically. Alas, Bayesian reasoning is not a panacea. Human irrationality can derail our attempts to use rational inference in numerous ways. Though our irrational biases cannot be eliminated, we can anticipate them and compensate for them. We can approach rational thinking the way we approach any occupation where there are safety hazards. We can develop safety checklists, habits, and policies that help us avoid faulty thinking. Fortunately, human irrationality is not random. Our irrationality has a lot of structure and predictability. We can use this structure to anticipate our errors and more readily correct them.

Our irrationality often takes the form of *cognitive biases*—proclivities that result in over- or under-estimation, over- or under-confidence, faulty expectations, neglect, and errors that sabotage our understanding. There are dozens of documented cognitive biases, and the experiments that demonstrate them are fascinating. I encourage you to read some of the entertaining and accessible books on cognitive bias that have been published in the last few years, including:

- *Thinking, Fast and Slow* by Daniel Kahneman (Macmillan, 2011)
- *Mistakes Were Made (But Not By Me): Why We Justify Foolish Beliefs, Bad Decisions, and Hurtful Acts* by Carol Tavris and Elliot Aronson (Houghton Mifflin, 2007)
- *Being Wrong: Adventures in the Margin of Error* by Kathryn Schulz (HarperCollins, 2010)
- *Bozo Sapiens: Why to Err is Human* by Ellen and Michael Kaplan (Bloomsbury Press, 2010)
- *Predictably Irrational: The Hidden Forces That Shape Our Decisions* by Dan Ariely (HarperCollins Canada, 2008)

My presentation is intended to be as concise and as compact as possible, so I will not catalog the cognitive biases. My goal is merely to show you a conceptual map of the territory and suggest some countermeasures.

Bayesian reasoning is prototypical reasoning, so it is natural to think that the countermeasure against our irrationality would be to simply think like a Bayesian. Indeed, Bayesian reasoning is a fantastic tool for finding flaws in our thinking. Unfortunately, Bayesian analysis is slow and time-consuming, and it is unrealistic to think that we can use it continuously. We cannot afford the time and energy to constantly check all of our beliefs against equations. It is more efficient to save

Bayesian analysis for high-stakes decisions and cases where we expect our intuition to make irrational judgments.

There is another reason a Bayesian analysis alone is likely to be insufficient. Humans are talented at making logical-sounding excuses for our beliefs and actions. This is called rationalization. If I give you nothing but Bayesian reasoning, you will likely use the technique to make better rationalizations—Bayesian-sounding excuses for what you want to believe.

We need to understand the nature of human irrationality to know when to apply Bayesian reasoning. We need to get a feel for when we are likely to think irrationally and how we can trick ourselves into reasoning instead of rationalizing.

I begin this section by describing how our thinking process works and how emotions help us make decisions. Then I will discuss the ways our emotions sometimes keep us clinging to bad ideas and blind us to the facts we need to know. I will discuss cognitive biases and how we can overcome them. We need to watch out for anything involving small probabilities, where our Neolithic brains will likely fail to understand reality.

I will discuss the subject of expertise. When is an expert an expert? When are we ourselves experts?

How do we defend ourselves against misinformation? I will outline the questions you can ask yourself to make sense of studies you read about in the media.

5.2   System One and System Two

In *Thinking, Fast and Slow*, Daniel Kahneman describes two broad categories of thinking, called *system one* and *system two*. System one thinking occurs rapidly, effortlessly, automatically, and largely subconsciously. When you watch a TV show, it requires almost no effort to understand the dialogue, identify the characters, and make emotional inferences about what the characters are feeling. We do not need pen and notebook to work out the plot, and we can figure out what is happening very quickly. Our minds simply recognize what is seen and heard and make rapid, automatic judgments. We can use system one for hours without feeling fatigued.

System two thinking involves self-guided focus and attention. System two thinking is used when we are doing our taxes or solving a mathematical puzzle. We also use system two when building furniture or systematically searching for someone in a crowd. Unlike system one thinking, system two thinking requires a lot of effort, proceeds slowly, and is difficult to do while multitasking. We easily become weary using system two. The wearier we become, the more prone we are to take shortcuts, lose focus, and make errors.

We make inferences during both system one and system two thinking, and both systems sometimes make errors in judgment and inference. Unlike system two, system one operates without conscious focus, and we are often unaware that system one is making inferences at all, let alone when it is making poor inferences.

For humans to be rational, we need to appreciate the roles and limitations of the two kinds of thinking and understand how to use system two to correct errors in system one reasoning. This is not because system two is more powerful than system one. Most of our cognitive ability is system one. However, because system two is conscious and deliberate, system two allows us to perform systematic checks and evaluations that are difficult with system one.

5.2.1   The Two Systems at Work

On a sunny day in San Diego in 2018, a doctor was driving through a residential neighborhood. While driving, he was on a phone call with his fiancée. He was also speeding. The doctor initially failed to notice two children crossing the street in front of his car.

This story does not have an ending because it is entirely fictitious, and I wrote it for demonstration purposes. In reading that four-sentence paragraph, your mind probably did not have time to paraphrase the story. However, your subconscious began to make intuitive judgments about the elements of the story. If your subconsciously formed beliefs were written down as explicit statements, they might resemble the following:

- The author mentioned that it was a sunny day. That must be relevant.

- The story takes place in San Diego. I imagine it was 75 degrees.

- Doctors are wealthy and drive nice cars. Perhaps this is a convertible.

- One should avoid talking on the phone while driving. To do so is careless and a sign of a person with a negligent personality.

- One should avoid speeding. Again, a sign of a negligent personality.

- Most of the conversations with one's fiancée are personal and not urgent. The doctor's attention should have been on the road.

- The doctor seems like a self-absorbed person.

These conclusions are the work of system one. Your mind did not have time to explicitly think of these statements while you read the four-sentence paragraph. Yet, your mind automatically reached these initial conclusions (or a set of conclusions comparable to these) without much effort or conscious awareness. And if I were to ask you to make some statements about the story and your interpretation of it, you could reply by making a list like the one above.

If I ask you to critique your beliefs about the story, you need to use system two. You need to explicitly write down your judgments, then step through the list and consider each judgment carefully. This requires you to guide your attention over each part of the story in turn, translating your intuitive understanding into explicit statements.

To the untrained mind, none of the explicit statements of subconscious inference seem wholly unreasonable. However, experiments tell us that system one judgments are frequently biased. For example, psychologists have discovered that when people make mistakes, we tend to attribute their error to flaws in their character instead of attributing their mistake to their situation. This bias is called *fundamental attribution error,* and it is a natural result of an asymmetry between what we know about ourselves and what we know about others. We know our own situation, so we can explain our own mistakes and shortfalls in terms of our circumstances. But we are generally unaware of all the situational causes of other people's mistakes, so we assume that other people's mistakes are a consequence of their flawed character.

In the story, the doctor intuitively seems negligent and self-absorbed. But how many of us have broken the speed limit? How many of us have answered calls from important people in our lives when we should have been focused on more important things?

Most of us have made such mistakes. Upon reflection, it therefore seems unreasonable to conclude from the few details in the story that this doctor is any more negligent and self-absorbed than you or I.

5.2.2 Mindfulness

System one is always at work, making vast numbers of implicit inferences from what it sees, hears, and reads. Consciously unpacking the contents of our intuitive judgments and testing them for accuracy are challenging and time-consuming. However, with practice, we not only become more aware of our subconscious judgments, we also train system one to look in on itself.

System one learns to recognize things through practice and feedback. With practice and mindfulness, we can develop a better intuition for when to use our conscious, system two thinking to make corrections.

5.3   The Role of Emotions in Decision Making

Brain injury patients whose prefrontal cortex has become disconnected from their emotion center are epistemically more rational than average. That is, their inferences are quite good. However, their injury ultimately prevents them from making simple decisions about what to do with that information.

Suppose you find yourself in an electronics store. There are TVs, radios, computers, and gaming consoles. Which of these products do you desire more? Which product would enhance your status with your friends? And which attribute of the system in question—price, size, performance—best suits your desires?

If your decision-making brain were cut off from your emotions, you would find that none of these questions were answerable. You could have excellent knowledge of the products, prices, and specifications yet be incapable of deciding what to buy or whether to buy at all.

Emotions convey vital information about our preferences to our decision-making center. For humans, emotions are indispensable. However, our emotions can also sabotage our thinking.

Suppose you spy the just-released gaming console on the store shelf. You are attracted to the machine's design and the allure of being the first of your friends to own one. The attractive sales assistant seems impressed by your interest in the product, too. All your emotions are now telling you to value this purchase above everything else—so much so that your emotions blind you to better choices you could make. You see only the arguments for buying the system, not the arguments for alternative products, better uses for the money, or shopping around for a better deal. Your arguments for buying the new gaming console may be correct, but because you only considered correct arguments for the purchase and not correct arguments against, your choice may have been irrational.

This is *motivated reasoning*, and it usually causes us to rationalize instead of reason. Rationalizing is giving excuses for a belief or decision in what appear to be logical arguments. An argument given as a rationalization may turn out to be sufficient reason—sufficient excuse—to have made the original judgment. But all too often, a rationalization is either a faulty argument or a hopelessly one-sided evaluation.

Proper reasoning is like a court trial. The lawyers for both sides give their arguments for their own sides, and the judge and jury weigh the evidence and arguments from both sides. When we rationalize, we take on the role of one of the lawyers; this makes it less likely that we will arrive at the truth. To be rational, we should take on the role of the judge and jury instead.

Be the judge and jury. Allow yourself to be swayed by the best case, for or against. Do not act like the lawyer.

5.4   Separating Fact and Opinion

Everyone is entitled to his own opinion, but not his own facts.
—Daniel Patrick Moynihan

In common culture, there is a grey area between facts and opinions. Most of us are more than happy to opine on almost any political or scientific controversy. Lately, it seems as if this grey area has been getting bigger. With the advent of blogs and social media, there are now thousands of media influencers who are more than happy to sell you their own boutique theory about the world. Selling a worldview on social media is now a trendy thing to do. Alas, most of this selling, and most of the buying, are epistemically irrational.

Consider the following questions that ask for your opinion:

Should we ban the death penalty unless we can guarantee we will never execute an innocent person?

Should women have the right to an abortion?

Should we give public money to private schools?

Should we increase marginal taxes on the wealthy?

Notice that each question incorporates the word *should*. These are moral questions. Facts have a bearing on the answers to such questions, but the facts are often insufficient to make the decision for us.

If a question is of a factual nature, it is not subject to opinion. A few questions relating to those same hot-button issues include:

Does the death penalty deter crime?

Does abortion cause psychological harm to the mother?

Do private schools outperform public schools?

Do low marginal taxes (taxes on the rich) reduce inequality?

If you have a political polarity, you may now feel a little rush of adrenaline as you prepare your arguments, pro or con. However, unless you are a sociologist with appreciation for the breadth of the research on these topics, you probably do not know the answers to these factual questions. If you are not an expert in sociology, it is better to admit your lack of expertise than to be overconfident.

Frequently, factual stories are not as relevant to moral questions as we think they are. As an exercise, consider the factual questions, decide what you believe the answers are, and then invert your answers. For example, if you believe the death penalty does not deter crime, imagine that it does. Likely, if you were opposed to the death penalty, you are still opposed to it, even after the fact is inverted. People who are opposed to the death penalty are generally not motivated by the dissuasive effect of capital punishment. People generally oppose capital punishment because they consider execution barbaric or because they are concerned about the inadvertent execution of the innocent. Yet, opponents of the death penalty would be likely to irrationally dismiss evidence that the death penalty deters crime because they would perceive such evidence as hostile to their moral opinions.

For the facts to become central in our political decision making, they need to be quite extreme. For example, if banning the death penalty doubled the crime rate, a lot of supporters of abolition might change their minds. Similarly, if private schools exacerbated inequality and consistently failed to meet the performance of public schools, a lot of advocates for private education would change their minds. Yet, in both of these examples, the facts are not so stark as to be decisive for most people with opinions on the matter.

Give up your fear of "hostile" facts. Recognize that your deeply held opinions often do not depend on facts, but rather on moral feelings.

When you give up your fear of hostile facts, you will reduce your anxiety, and science will become your friend. You will comfortably accept good studies that pose a problem for your opinions, and honestly critique weak studies that seem to support your point of view.

Once you begin to let go of your fear, you can think about what sorts of hypothetical evidence would change your mind. For example, taxing the rich at lower rates than the poor seems unfair, but would you accept low marginal tax rates if, hypothetically, it was proven that such "unfair" rates ultimately reduced inequality?

Try to imagine the hypothetical evidence that could sway your moral opinion.

5.5   Heuristics and Biases

Our political positions are shaped by our informal judgments. Where are the dangers in this world, and what can we do about them? What is human nature, and how can we structure society to help people reach their full potential?

To answer these questions, we rely on what we read in the news media. Yet, unless we are making an in-depth study of the sociological literature, we are probably making poorly informed judgments. When we work with uncertainty and small probabilities, our cognitive biases come into play.

Brains have evolved shortcuts that help us make decisions using less effort and fewer calculations. These shortcuts are known as *heuristics*, and they allow us to massively simplify the task of inference. However, heuristics are only approximations. When they fail, we end up with a bias—a systematically incorrect answer.

The great danger of biases is that they provide us with false confidence. Our heuristics deliver common sense answers in scenarios where we get rapid feedback about our errors. Yet these same estimation instincts can result in profound irrationality when applied to situations where we do not get frequent corrective feedback and situations that involve extreme statistics.

One of these heuristics is the availability heuristic. Estimating probability accurately requires perfect recall and time-consuming tabulation of mental records. For example, if you were going fishing at the river today, what is the probability that you will catch a fish?

To answer this question accurately, you need to recall the number of times you fished in the river and caught a fish and divide by the total number of times you fished. Of course, you might even be able to improve your estimate by factoring in weather, water temperature, and the precise number of hours you spent fishing on each occasion. Unfortunately, a normal human cannot remember more than a handful of individual events nor maintain a count of hits and misses.

The brain solves this problem by answering a different question, "How easily can I recall instances of catching a fish?"

To use this heuristic, we do not have to remember vast quantities of data; we need only remember one or more examples of the event. If you remember catching a fish last Thursday, and you fish every day, you have a crude estimate of the probability of catching a fish today.

Of course, our recall is biased by many factors. Events that occurred recently are easier to recall, as are events that evoke powerful emotional responses. Thus, our estimates of probability are inaccurate, especially when estimating the probability of rare or emotionally salient events. We are prone to overestimate the frequency of highly memorable events and underestimate the probability of more mundane occurrences.

The availability heuristic distorts our estimates of prior probabilities and likelihoods. If we ask ourselves to judge the frequency of events without referring to tabulated data, we are likely to end up with incorrect probability estimates.

Another crude shortcut that the brain takes in estimating probabilities is the representativeness heuristic, which judges the probability that a person belongs to a certain class by how much they resemble the stereotype of that class. This is precisely the problem that we looked at in the previous chapter when we posed the question:

Dave wears glasses and is an introvert. Is Dave more likely a salesperson or a librarian?

People tend to answer such questions by comparing Dave to the stereotypical images of a librarian and a salesperson. Dave is clearly a better match for the stereotypical image of a librarian, so it makes intuitive sense to us that Dave is probably a librarian. This kind of thinking is flawed, and we can see why by applying Bayesian reasoning.

Our theories are:

T_S: Dave is a salesperson.

T_L: Dave is a librarian.

Our evidence is wearing glasses and being an introvert:

E: Dave wears glasses and is an introvert.

The stereotype is that this evidence is the hallmark of being a librarian:

$$P(E|T_L) = high$$

Meanwhile, glasses and introversion are not part of the stereotype of a salesperson:

$$P(E|T_S) = low$$

Many stereotypes are false or misleading. However, as we saw earlier, even assuming the stereotypes are truthful, the representativeness heuristic is going to lead us to the wrong conclusion from time to time. The representativeness heuristic takes the stereotype and turns it on its head. In Bayesian terms, the representativeness heuristic leaps from a likelihood to a posterior probability:

$$P(T_L|E) = P(E|T_L) = high \qquad (representativeness\ heuristic)$$

The heuristic says that if librarians are introverts who wear glasses, then introverts who wear glasses are likely librarians. This is a fallacy. By converting a likelihood into a posterior, our heuristic has given no thought to our priors. What we should be doing is thinking through the whole Bayesian inference:

$$P(T_L|E) = \frac{P(T_L)P(E|T_L)}{P(T_L)P(E|T_L) + P(T_S)P(E|T_S)}$$

When we substitute our naïve stereotypes for our likelihoods, we end up with:

$$P(T_L|E) = \frac{P(T_L)\ high}{P(T_L)\ high + P(T_S)\ low}$$

If our priors are equal, $P(T_L) = P(T_S)$, the heuristic has reached a reasonable conclusion. As we saw earlier, the priors are not equal. We can query our priors with a variation on the original question:

> Dave is a person. Which is more likely, that Dave is a salesperson or a librarian?

As we saw in our earlier presentation of this problem, salespeople are around 100 times more common than librarians. Unless glasses wearing and introversion are incredibly rare among salespeople, there is no way the stereotype could override the low priors—and this assumes the stereotype is even true in the first place.

Sometimes, the representativeness heuristic can even trick us into believing something impossible. In a classic study by Tversky and Kahneman, [18] undergraduate students were asked the following question:

---

[18] Tversky, Amos; Kahneman, Daniel (October 1983). "Extension versus intuitive reasoning: The conjunction fallacy in probability judgment". Psychological Review. 90 (4): 293–315. doi:10.1037/0033-295X.90.4.293.

Linda is 31 years old, single, outspoken, and very bright. She majored in philosophy. As a student, she was deeply concerned with issues of discrimination and social justice, and also participated in anti-nuclear demonstrations.

Which is more probable?

a.   Linda is a bank teller.

b.   Linda is a bank teller and is active in the feminist movement.

The majority of students rated (b) as more likely than (a). Yet (b) cannot possibly be more likely. Bank tellers active in the feminist movement are a subset of all bank tellers. At best, the two probabilities could be equal, and realistically (a) is more probable than (b). This error is known as the *conjunction fallacy*—the mistaken conclusion that the probability of being in the whole is smaller than the probability of being in the subset.

There are several candidate explanations for why people fall prey to the conjunction fallacy, but it seems probable that the representativeness heuristic is playing a trick on us. Bank teller does not match the stereotype for an activist, whereas an activist bank teller does.

Stereotypes are a hazard to rationality. They are offensive to the stereotyped group and cause us to prejudge people in irrational ways. Stereotypes are no substitute for sound statistical analysis.

Let's examine one more heuristic. When asked to estimate a number or value, we typically do so by first *anchoring* on a value we have seen recently and then correcting from our anchoring point. Anchoring is a psychological effect that has been studied for more than 60 years.

If I were to ask you how many distinct musical artists made it to number one on the Billboard Pop Charts between 1985 and 1987, you are quite unlikely to know the exact answer. Instead, you would need to make a guess, partially informed by the bands you can think of, the number of weeks in the year, and the average number of weeks a song would have remained at number one. The curious thing is that the answer you give may well depend on the number, 60, that I quoted in the prior paragraph! Obviously, the number of years that psychologists have been studying anchoring has absolutely nothing to do with the number of bands reaching number one in the mid-1980s. Yet, the brain is susceptible to this subtle form of suggestion. If I had falsely stated in the prior paragraph that psychologists had been studying anchoring for 30 years, your estimate of the number of number one artists would likely have been smaller.

Experiments demonstrate that we often estimate values by making an initial guess that serves as an anchor, and then updating our guess by incorporating facts that come to mind. Research suggests that our initial anchor is sensitive to numbers that we are exposed to when the question is asked, even unrelated numbers. Moreover, it seems that we tend to under-correct from our anchor point based on facts that come to our attention after the anchoring.

The last few pages describe just three of the hundred or so cognitive biases that have been documented. The takeaway from these examples is that sticking to beliefs based on your gut impression is generally irrational. Combine gut impressions with irrational escalation, and you will soon find yourself defending a faulty belief just to save your ego and social status.

Treat your intuitive reaction as merely the starting point for a rational investigation. Do not commit your ego or status to them. Instead, look at the statistics and the uncertainties.

5.6   An Argument From Authority

Critical thinking courses teach us a list of logical fallacies—errors in deductive reasoning. We are warned that an argument from authority is one of the fallacies, and just because someone is an authority does not mean that what they say is necessarily true. Indeed, there are many instances where doctors, scientists, government analysts, or journalists have gotten their facts wrong.

However, there is a critical difference between a logical fallacy and an inductive fallacy. A logical fallacy asks if error is possible. An inductive fallacy asks if error is probable. As we will see, trust in expertise is often justified. The challenge is to understand the conditions under which that trust is justified.

For any incorrect point of view, one can usually find an expert who is willing to take its side. The expert may simply be mistaken, or they may be willing to advocate for the faulty view in exchange for compensation. There are groups with a vested interest in making consumers and voters think that settled science is not settled and that extraordinary claims are not being made by their side of the debate. How are we to tell which expert opinions to trust?

5.6.1   The Consensus of Experts

Science is a cultural practice. Though scientists strive to be rational and systematic, the main thing keeping them aligned with reality is their engagement with the scientific community. In the academic sciences, social status is earned by doing responsible research that produces lasting insight. Science advances in large part because scientists critique each other's work and build on the work of their peers. When scientists disagree, they engage with each other constructively by acknowledging the strengths and weaknesses of each other's theories.

Individually, scientists are as human as you or I. They are susceptible to biases and motivated reasoning, just like the rest of us. When scientists step into any other area of their lives, they are vulnerable to many of the same cognitive biases that affect laypersons. Indeed, scientific rationality is often compartmentalized. A scientist may follow strict protocols for eliminating bias in their lab yet find themselves superstitious in other contexts.

As a result, whether they are experimentalists or theoreticians, investigators rarely work effectively on science in isolation. A scientist who works in seclusion is prone to devise ideas that have already been contradicted by experiment or that violate logical principles. There may be obvious flaws in their ideas, but without a circle of collaborators to review their work, there is no one who can tell them where they have gone wrong. Before they know it, they have invested their efforts and egos into a project that should never have gotten off the ground.

Occasionally, loners may portray themselves as scientific heroes who have been unjustly cast out from the priesthood of mainstream scientists. However, this narrative is nonsense. Any new theory that comes along is fertile ground for up-and-coming scientists to make a name for themselves, so long as the theory is logical and consistent with experiment. If the theory is illogical or contradicts experiment, it is normal and expected that the purveyor of the theory will fail to gain acceptance in the community. Ideas are excluded from the mainstream because they have no merit, not simply because they are new or novel.

Indeed, scientists are comfortable with advancing radical new ideas. A scientist can admit that their theory is a long shot and publish a paper in good faith, explaining how their theory might have evaded experimental test or detection thus far. However, if a scientist simply contradicts mainstream, proven ideas, they are unlikely to get anywhere. And this is how it should be. A scientist whose theory contradicts an established mainstream theory is making an extraordinary claim. If they are to publish a paper in a refereed journal, they need to bring extraordinary evidence to the table.

When you read about a scientist who contradicts the consensus of experts in his field, who claims to be exiled from the "priesthood" of scientists, you are almost certainly looking at a person pushing an irrational theory. They will have their followers, typically people who have religious or ideological beliefs that would be bolstered if the scientific consensus collapsed. They may even have some wealthy sponsors. But do not believe them until they can win over the scientific consensus.

As laypersons, the most rational belief we can hold is that of the scientific consensus.

5.6.2   A Story of Personal Error

In July 2020, while the United States was suffering through the beginnings of the COVID-19 pandemic, *Newsweek* published an op-ed[19] by Harvey Risch, a medical doctor and epidemiologist at the Yale School of Public Health. Risch argued that, contrary to the warnings and directives of the medical establishment and public health officials, doctors should prescribe a combination of hydroxychloroquine (HCQ) and zinc plus an antibiotic at the earliest stages of COVID-19 infection. Risch argued that the key to the success of the treatment as an antiviral is early treatment, and prior studies showing HCQ to be ineffective or dangerous were primarily looking at its effects on patients who were already

---

[19] Harvey A. Risch (July 23 2020). The Key to Defeating COVID-19 Already Exists. We Need to Start Using It. Newsweek,

https://www.newsweek.com/key-defeating-covid-19-already-exists-we-need-start-using-it-opinion-1519535.

hospitalized. In his op-ed, Risch invited readers to look at his paper published in *American Journal of Epidemiology*.[20] What are we to make of this claim?

I cite this example for two reasons. First, I was deceived by it long enough to post a link to the op-ed on social media. For this reason, I think the judgment is worth a post mortem. Second, I made a mistake—an embarrassing mistake for the author of a book on rational thinking—and I think it is important to accept and acknowledge our mistakes. If we minimize our errors, we will not learn from them.

Amid the pandemic, HCQ became a political football. For those wanting to prioritize the reopening of economic and social activity, the promise of HCQ was alluring. If we could all take doses of HCQ and go about our lives as usual, businesses could reopen and life could continue as normal. Initially, the medical community shared these hopes. Early in the pandemic, doctors in China noticed that people taking HCQ for autoimmune illnesses were less susceptible to the SARS-CoV-2 virus. Perhaps an existing, approved drug would be effective as an antiviral.

---

[20] Harvey A Risch (2020). Early Outpatient Treatment of Symptomatic, High-Risk Covid-19 Patients that Should be Ramped-Up Immediately as Key to the Pandemic Crisis. American Journal of Epidemiology, https://doi.org/10.1093/aje/kwaa093.

Moreover, HCQ was thought to enable dietary zinc to enter the cells, and zinc was known to suppress viral replication. On paper and in the test tube, it seemed like the combination could work. The medical community and the World Health Organization (WHO) encouraged physicians to test the drug, and the Federal Drug Administration (FDA) gave doctors special dispensation to use it for treating COVID-19 patients.

Nevertheless, the more studies that came out on the use of HCQ and the better those studies became, the less the drug appeared to be effective.[21] In some studies, patients on HCQ fared worse than patients not on the drug.[22] Consequently, both WHO and FDA withdrew their endorsements and special dispensation for the drug. Still, few of the studies on HCQ involved zinc, and most of the studies had opportunities for bias, for example, by having nonrandom criteria for

---

[21] Boulware DR, Pullen MF, Bangdiwala AS, Pastick KA, Lofgren SM, Okafor EC, et al. (June 2020). *A Randomized Trial of Hydroxychloroquine as Postexposure Prophylaxis for Covid-19*. N. Engl. J. Med. 383 (6): 517–525. doi:10.1056/NEJMoa2016638.

[22] Horby, Peter, et al. *Effect of Hydroxychloroquine in Hospitalized Patients with COVID-19: Preliminary Results from a Multi-Centre, Randomized, Controlled Trial*. MedRxiv, Cold Spring Harbor Laboratory Press, 1 Jan. 2020 https://www.medrxiv.org/content/10.1101/2020.07.15.20151852v1.

administering the drug. Could the drug be much more effective if administered early and in conjunction with zinc?

All this information was in my head before I read Prof. Risch's op-ed. Here was a qualified epidemiologist from a prestigious institution, citing research in an epidemiology journal. He was citing studies of HCQ and zinc given early after infection, research that seemed to show that the treatment was effective. I posted a link to the op-ed and the journal article, "HCQ + Zinc seems to work in outpatient settings. By the time you are hospitalized, the success is mixed."

Three hours later, a friend posted a link to an article at *Science-Based Medicine*[23] that was devastatingly critical of the op-ed as well as Risch's journal article. I immediately recognized that I had made an error in posting the op-ed. Where had I gone wrong?

I made four major mistakes. The lesser of these mistakes was not probing the research further. I had not read the entire journal article nor checked its citations before posting a link to it on social media. It turns out that the studies cited by

---

[23] David Gorski (2020). *Hydroxychloroquine to treat COVID-19: Evidence can't seem to kill it,* Science-Based Medicine, July 27 2020 https://sciencebasedmedicine.org/hydroxychloroquine-to-treat-covid-19-evidence-cant-seem-to-kill-it.

Risch were utterly abysmal, and his reasoning was flawed.[24] Had I investigated the studies cited by Risch, I would easily have recognized that they were hopelessly flawed.

My second error was being deceived by Risch's credentials and the platform he was given by *Newsweek*. I assumed that no legitimate epidemiologist would commit such errors. *Newsweek* has historically had some reliability when it comes to news reporting, but even the best news media have much lower standards of reliability when it comes to their opinion and editorial pages.

The third error I made was in overestimating my expertise. I am not an expert in the study of viruses, the immune system, patient treatment, medical research practices, or drug design. While I am quite fluent in the general theory of biases and experimental design, there were other flaws in Risch's paper that I would not have noticed.

The fourth and greatest error I made was in neglecting the consensus of experts while implicitly promoting a public policy. By reposting the op-ed and the journal

---

[24] See for example, Frits R. Rosendaal, *Review of: "Hydroxychloroquine and azithromycin as a treatment of COVID-19: results of an open-label non-randomized clinical trial Gautret et al 2010"*,

https://doi.org/10.1016/j.ijantimicag.2020.106063

(http://www.sciencedirect.com/science/article/pii/S0924857920302338).

article on social media (albeit for only three hours), I spread misinformation. The consensus of medical experts is that HCQ does not work, and I am in no position to contradict their conclusion.

There is ongoing research into HCQ and cocktails of HCQ with other drugs. Perhaps that research will one day find that it is effective in the early stages of COVID-19. However, as it stands, the case for HCQ is extremely weak.

The takeaway from this experience is that even experienced critical thinkers sometimes commit errors of reasoning. Rationality is hard work, and it is easy to become complacent or let fatigue get the better of you. Instead of viewing yourself as a competent judge of a story's reliability, start from a position of humility. If posting faulty information on social media incurred a $50 fine, would you still post the story? Or would you wait for expert, accredited verification?

Keep a list of recently corrected beliefs—beliefs that you held until corrected by evidence and rational inference to the contrary.

5.6.3   Sometimes There Is No Consensus

Sometimes, there is no expert consensus. For example, there is no strong expert consensus as to whether there is intelligent life elsewhere in our galaxy. It is certainly plausible and worthy of investigation, but there is insufficient evidence to convince most scientists to take that bet. Another example is the existence of a multiverse. Multiverses appear in many cosmological models, so discussion about their existence is mainstream. However, until a multiverse model makes a strong and successful prediction, physicists will lack confidence in any specific multiverse theory.

Just because experts discuss an idea or publish speculative papers does not mean the idea is part of the expert consensus.

5.6.4   Pundits Versus Predictors

What are your hobbies and interests? Do you consider yourself an expert? You are likely well-informed about your interests and recent developments. However, if you have predictive theories about what will happen in the future or what techniques are optimal, your intuitive theories are likely to be poor predictors unless you are getting rapid corrective feedback of your errors and tracking your success rate in making predictions.

This typically causes us to overestimate the ability of experts. Their background knowledge impresses us, and we assume their background knowledge translates into the ability to make accurate predictions.

Though we may feel like an expert based on our background knowledge, our intuition is likely to lead us to irrational predictions unless we receive frequent, personal correction in our daily experience. The word correction is critical. When we lack correction, even frequent experience and knowledge may lead to irrational judgments and overconfidence.

A physician working in a hospital will likely have predictive expertise about the common diagnoses among her patients. Common diagnoses are, by definition, frequent in her experience, and if the physician is putting her intuitive judgments to the test with objective lab testing, the physician is receiving frequent feedback on her intuitive diagnoses. That is, when the physician makes a faulty intuitive judgment, she will receive rapid feedback about the error and learn from her experience.

However, if the same physician encounters a patient with a rare condition, the physician's intuition will likely lead to an inaccurate intuitive diagnosis. Though the physician may get regular daily diagnostic feedback about common conditions, the physician will have had little feedback about diagnosing rare conditions. Moreover, since the condition is rare, the physician will be forced to estimate a tiny probability outside the range where our intuition functions reliably.

In their best-selling book, *Superforecasting: The Art and Science of Prediction*,[25] Philip E. Tetlock and Dan Gardner report on what it takes to make accurate predictions about future events. Tetlock worked with amateur volunteers to find out what it would take to accurately predict geopolitical events based on news and intelligence reports. One of the most important factors is to state predictions precisely so that feedback can be generated and graded in a timely fashion. For example, the prediction that the U.S. will institute a single-payer health care

---

[25] Philip E. Tetlock and Dan Gardner (2015). *Superforecasting: The Art and Science of Prediction*. Crown. ISBN 0804136696.

delivery system is too vague and open-ended to be tested. If the U.S. does not institute such a system in four years, the statement might still end up being true. Instead, a more testable prediction will specify a deadline, for example, "The U.S. will institute a single-payer health care delivery system by the end of the next presidential term." To get good at making predictions, we need to get rapid negative feedback about bad predictions.

Political pundits have all the trappings of experts. They are treated as authorities on politics and speak with confidence and conviction. They are well-informed about political processes and know who's who in the political world. It seems natural that pundits would be good at predicting political outcomes such as electoral, legislative, or geopolitical success. However, this turns out not to be the case. Success for a pundit comes in the form of popularity and contracts for op-eds with news organizations. In general, pundits are not graded according to the accuracy of their predictions. Indeed, most pundits do not even make specific predictions with time frames. Tetlock and Gardner report that political pundits do not perform much better than chance.

Train yourself to make good predictions by making predictions that can be graded on a deadline. Your opinions about future events or social policies are liable to be inaccurate unless you have received rapid and frequent corrections about mistaken predictions in the past.

5.6.5   Assessing Your Own Expertise

The most obvious way to judge your own expertise in a topic is to see if other people know all the background knowledge and trivia that you know. If you spend a weekend watching YouTube videos about Nicola Tesla, you are probably going to be an expert on Nicola Tesla relative to 99% of the people you know. However, if this is all you know about electromagnetism, your expertise on the viability of Nicola Tesla's ideas will be nearly zero.

In popular culture, Tesla is regarded as a genius who possessed secrets that even the scientists of today have yet to discover. In the later period of his life, Tesla was indeed working on a system of wireless delivery of electrical power. According to a popular narrative, if only Tesla had not been sidelined by his enemies or succumbed to mental illness, we would all be using Tesla's wireless electrical energy by now.

However, the means to transmit electrical energy wirelessly is not a secret at all. James Clerk Maxwell's equations governing electrical waves in space were published in 1865, and his theory was quite mature by 1873. The science of electrical power radiation was well-understood almost two decades before Tesla began his wireless transmission experiments in 1890. We do not use Tesla's wireless power transmission because it does not work effectively.

The lesson here is not to judge your expertise against your non-expert peers. Instead, if you have time, take a closer look at the courses and training that the true experts completed while earning their qualifications. In a technical field, it takes years to complete a graduate degree, and the best experts have years of original research on top of that training. This will provide you with better judgment about your level of expertise.

In 1999, David Dunning and Justin Kruger published a paper titled, "Unskilled and Unaware of It: How Difficulties in Recognizing One's Own Incompetence Lead to Inflated Self-Assessments,"[26] in which they describe what has come to be known as the Dunning-Kruger Effect. When we lack expertise, we lack the ability to judge that expertise. Our confidence in our own expertise rises rapidly when we first dive in and get some familiarity with a topic. As we delve deeper and study research papers in the field, we see other brilliant minds struggling with deep questions, and we begin to understand how little we know. This causes our initial high confidence to fall. If we develop our expertise to a more professional level, our confidence level rises again.

Do not judge your expertise relative to other non-experts. Remember the Dunning-Kruger effect. When you know relatively little, you are likely to overestimate your expertise.

---

[26] Kruger, Justin; Dunning, David (1999). *Unskilled and Unaware of It: How Difficulties in Recognizing One's Own Incompetence Lead to Inflated Self-Assessments.* Journal of Personality and Social Psychology. 77 (6): 1121–1134. https://doi.org/10.1037/0022-3514.77.6.1121. PMID 10626367.

5.7   The Experts Got It Wrong

In America, there is a growing, irrational distain for experts. This seems to be fueled by the atmosphere of partisan polarization and political populism. It is also driven partly by predictions that have failed to come true. In this section, we will explore failures or apparent failures of expertise.

5.7.1   Good Eggs and Bad Eggs

Do you remember when eggs were declared unhealthy because they contain cholesterol? Now they are healthy again? What does this say about experts?

Decades ago, it was discovered that high blood cholesterol was correlated with heart disease and arterial plaque. Scientists assumed that the cholesterol was absorbed directly from the food we eat, and since eggs contain significant cholesterol, eggs were viewed as a risky food. However, it was later discovered that we do not absorb much cholesterol directly from the foods we eat. Instead, our foods are broken down during digestion, and most of our cholesterols are produced from the raw materials when we consume fat.

There have been numerous studies of eggs that have appeared in the media, with seemingly conflicting outcomes. Why can't the experts decide what is true?

Large, long-term dietary studies cannot be randomized for control. No one would join a two-year study in which they will be told either to eat eggs daily or to abstain from eggs altogether. Instead, these studies are mostly observational (i.e., they observe people doing what they normally do) and ask them about their diets. However, health and diet are affected by a multitude of factors. For example, if you cook with eggs at home, you may be wealthier or have more free time for family or leisure, a lifestyle that could influence your health.

In an observational study, researchers do their best to control for the various factors that can affect health, but they are unlikely to completely isolate them all. If eggs have little or no effect on cardiovascular health, the study might produce a zero correlation, but it might also produce a small positive or negative correlation by chance. The media will report this as "eggs are good for you" or "eggs are bad for you" without clearly identifying how big the effect is. Recall what we said in section 4.11 about experimental evidence for weak effects, and how study outcomes fail to converge on a positive result. If moderate egg consumption has a very weak effect on health, we may expect some experiments to show no effect, some to show a small positive effect, and some to show a small negative effect.

The latest studies show that eating half an egg per day raises your chances of getting cardiovascular disease or diabetes by less than 10%, a relatively small effect.[27] For comparison, smokers get heart disease at a rate 200%–400% above normal. If studies of a cause-effect relationship are inconclusive or bounce

---

[27] Zhong VW, Van Horn L, Cornelis MC, et al. *Associations of Dietary Cholesterol or Egg Consumption With Incident Cardiovascular Disease and Mortality*. JAMA. 2019;321(11):1081–1095. doi:10.1001/jama.2019.1572.

between yes and no, it may be because there is no strong cause-effect relationship, and studies are responding to random noise in the data.

5.7.2   The Experts Are in on It!

When outsiders dislike the expert consensus, they sometimes accuse the experts of being part of a mass conspiracy to conceal the truth. As we discussed in the last section, the social incentive structure in the sciences makes grand conspiracy theories virtually impossible. Scientists gain status by creating long-lived theories that accurately predict outcomes and get cited by future scientists. Faking results does occur from time to time, and sometimes the community is fooled for a time, but such events are rare and, ultimately, the fakery is exposed. Moreover, scientists are not paid enough to see economic benefit by participating in the conspiracy. They stand to make more money and status by exposing conspiracies than by participating in them.

Accusations of mass conspiracy in the sciences are a hallmark of pseudoscience.

5.7.3   If the Experts Are Right...

...there will still be anomalies.

Believers in the supernatural or the paranormal like to point to the unexplained as evidence for their alternative theories. If the experts are so smart, why can't they explain every data point, every photograph, or every eyewitness account?

No matter how secure our knowledge, there will always be something that remains to be explained. The mystery may be due to a measurement error, hallucination, hoax, or delusion. Evolutionary biologists have thousands of data points mapping out how life evolved on our planet. We can see the evidence in living species, the fossil record, DNA, simulations, and experiments. Opponents of the theory say there are gaps in the fossil record. Of course there are gaps! Only a tiny proportion of animals fall into the kinds of mud and tar that will preserve their bodies and skeletons, and only a fraction of those animals will survive erosion and other forces that might destroy their fossils. It is not a prediction of evolutionary biology that there will be no gaps. The prediction is that all animals will de descended from similar animals, that we are all related, that we are all made of comparable materials, and that the process takes millions of years. All of these predictions have been confirmed over and over. Intelligent design does not predict these things, and that is why belief in intelligent design is irrational.

Indeed, we played out this very scenario in our game of Six-Twenty. Recall that the D6 theory had been overwhelmingly supported by the evidence until a 14 appeared in the data. The 14 is certainly an anomaly for the D6 theory. Perhaps the roll of the six-sided die was misread, misstated, or misheard. We calculated the probabilities and discovered that the isolated anomaly was insufficient evidence to displace the D6 theory. Even if we never find the ultimate explanation for the 14 that appeared in our data, the anomaly is insufficient on its own to displace our well-established theory.

Isolated anomalies in the evidence are not unusual. Well-established theories tolerate them.

5.7.4   Groupthink

Groupthink is a cognitive bias in which a group of collaborators become fixated on one single theory or point of view for the sake of harmony and group cohesion. This is a cognitive bias that can take hold of experts, especially when they work together in a single organization.

On February 1, 2003, the Space Shuttle Columbia broke up during re-entry. It was discovered that, during launch, a piece of insulating foam had broken off from the main fuel tank and struck the left wing, knocking off heat-resistant tiles. When the orbiter returned to Earth, the heat of re-entry cut into the wing where the tiles were missing. Later investigations found that consultants had written memos to NASA staff warning of a potential disaster.[28] Why had NASA not acted on the information?

NASA developed a culture that rejected outside criticism, making it difficult for alternative views to be heard. When an organization cultivates a single viewpoint

---

[28] John Schwartz and Matthew L. Wald, *NASA's Curse?; 'Groupthink' Is 30 Years Old, And Still Going Strong*, New York Times, March 9, 2003.

in the name of cohesion, accurate assessment becomes difficult.[29] Though NASA was packed with experts, the project management culture did not allow for diversity in viewpoints.

In the academic sciences, groupthink is uncommon. Though researchers engage in collaborative discourse, they are also competitors looking for ways to make a name for themselves in more successful lines of research. In most scientific fields, you will find healthy debate and a diversity of viewpoints.

5.7.5 Fear, Uncertainty, and Doubt

For decades, tobacco companies denied that cigarettes cause disease. Tobacco companies found experts who were willing to make technical arguments for their case. For example, it was argued that perhaps the high correlation between smoking and lung cancer was not an example of smoking causing cancer. Instead, apologists for tobacco argued that a genetic predisposition may have caused both the cancer and the predisposition to smoke cigarettes. By this logic, perhaps the cancer was not smoking's fault because bearers of this condition were likely to get cancer even without smoking cigarettes.

---

[29] Dimitroff, R. D., Schmidt, L. A., & Bond, T. D. (2005). *Organizational behavior and disaster: a study of conflict at NASA.* Project Management Journal, 36(2), 28–38.

For smokers and for the businesses that profited from tobacco, this was just what they were motivated to believe. In the face of numerous health warnings, smokers could use this shred of doubt as a buttress against feeling foolish for continuing to smoke tobacco. Though it is deductively possible for the gene theory to have been true, it was inductively improbable. Still, tobacco company denials were relatively effective at staving off lawsuits and government regulations. Many thousands of people died because the corporations that profited from tobacco stirred up enough doubt in the scientific consensus. In fact, internal tobacco company memos showed that the corporations knew the health risks to consumers yet publicly denied the risks to protect their bottom line.[30]

Tobacco is not the only industry to engage in this practice. Internal memos reveal that Exxon knew about global warming and its consequences in 1977, and the oil company knew it was harming Earth's climate even before it became a political issue.[31] Since then, Exxon and other oil firms have invested millions of

---

[30] World Health Organization. (2004). *The Tobacco Industry Documents. What they are, what they tell us and how to search them. A Practical Manual (2nd Edition)*. Center for Tobacco Control Research and Education, UC San Francisco, University of California at San Francisco, Center for Tobacco Control Research and Education.

[31] Hall, S. *Exxon Knew about Climate Change Almost 40 Years Ago*, Scientific American, Oct 26, 2015.

dollars promoting fringe "experts" and sowing doubt about the scientific consensus.

Business interests are not the only forces that fight scientific consensus. There are special interest groups that oppose vaccination and genetically modified foods. These groups also front their own "expert witnesses" willing to testify about the dangers and seize upon any little study that might discredit their target. For example, a 2012 paper by Gilles-Eric Séralini appeared to show that Monsanto's genetically modified corn caused significantly more tumors in rats than non-GMO corn. Rats and humans are different, but if GMO corn did cause cancer in humans, we would have expected human cancer rates in the United States to have skyrocketed, as GMO corn is ubiquitous in the U.S. market. Instead, cancer rates fell. Thus, even if Séralini's research were accurate with respect to the corn's effect on rats, it was inconsistent with observed effects in humans. Ultimately, in 2013, Séralini's paper was retracted by the publisher for failing to reach statistical significance.[32] Part of the reason that Séralini's paper caused so much fuss was that the toxicology of GMO corn had already been studied on a larger scale, and an effect as large as Séralini reported would not likely have gone unnoticed. Séralini's claim was an extraordinary one.

---

[32] Wallace Hayes A (2014). *Editor in Chief of Food and Chemical Toxicology answers questions on retraction.* Food Chem. Toxicol. 65: 394–5. doi:10.1016/j.fct.2014.01.006. PMID 24407018.

As a rule, side with the scientific consensus, particularly the consensus of scientists who work in the field in question. The scientific consensus is right more often than it is wrong, and when it is wrong, it is still more rational than individuals and amateurs.

Still, we need to find criteria for judging the evidence presented by scientists and cynics. This is the topic of the next section.

5.8 Defending Yourself Against Misinformation

Online media is flooded with misinformation, sometimes by well-meaning parties who wish to call attention to risk or injustice, and sometimes by corporations or governments with darker objectives in mind. There are also excellent sources of news and information. How do we tell the good from the bad?

When it comes to journalism, the most professional organizations have a strong culture of journalistic ethics. Larger news organizations have an ombudsman, an office or authority that will investigate claims of unethical practices. When stories are found to be flawed, they publish corrections or retract the story. The Society of Professional Journalists has a code of ethics intended to focus reporters on seeking truth, avoiding conflicts of interest, minimizing harm to the public, and maintaining accountability. Among the guidelines, journalists should distinguish news from advertising, refuse favors that damage their credibility, and use material from unnamed sources only where necessary. Not all journalists follow these rules, but professional news organizations such as *The Wall Street Journal* and *The New York Times* maintain high standards for their reporters. Sometimes, journalists make mistakes, but professional news organizations hold their staff accountable for error.

Contrast professional news organizations with social commentators, bloggers, and organizations with political objectives. A journalist working for a website dedicated to political or ideological perspective will likely tell their story in a way that paints their ideological opponents in a bad light. If their organization has a nonexistent code of ethics or a weak culture of enforcement, they will not have incentive to accurately report the truth. Indeed, they may be rewarded by their management for writing stories that generate clicks, sell advertising, or effect political outreach.

Ad Fontes Media [33] publishes a chart that positions news organizations according to their political leanings and their degree of journalistic reliability. Professional news organizations occupy the top center of the chart because they do original fact reporting and reliably attempt to report on both sides of every issue. Organizations on the left and right wings of the chart are essentially propaganda organizations, and their reliability is correspondingly low.

---

[33] https://www.adfontesmedia.com.

If you read about a conspiracy theory on a blog or partisan news source, and none of the professional media organizations touch the story, it is because the story is unsubstantiated and bogus. Professional media organizations should be your primary news source. If they will not report on what should be an important story, there is probably not enough evidence to make the story rationally believable.

There is one important caveat. Professional news organizational typically have a political agenda that is reflected in their opinions and editorials pages. Often, opinions are written by nonjournalists who are not bound by the rules of professional journalism. In other words, expect editorials and opinion pieces to be heavily biased. A media organization's bias may also be reflected in the stories they choose to tell and the way the stories are told.

Popular science media outlets want you to click on their stories and read them. This means they want to make the research sound as interesting and as impactful as possible. Unfortunately, this often means that the impact of the study being quoted is likely to be overblown. A small study with little impact may be wrongly portrayed as revolutionary. This is dangerous. Many people will seize on any science story, no matter how inconsequential, to justify their personal habits or political inclinations. To get a handle on the real strength of the evidence, here are a few criteria to consider.

If the study is about physics, chemistry, biology, climate, or other hard sciences, you need to gauge the consensus of the experts in the field. Theoretical studies are cheap. A single investigator can perform an analysis, write a paper, and put out a press release. There may be nothing wrong with the analysis, but if it is pure speculation, it might be more entertainment that scientific contribution. With theoretical papers, the key is to gauge what the author's peers are saying about the research. Some theoretical work results in a true breakthrough, altering the way theoreticians will perform research in the future.

As for experimental evidence in the hard sciences, one factor to look for is the size and budget of the experiment. If an experiment has a large scale and a large budget, the investigators must have convinced enough of their peers that their work was a priority. Even if a large research project is speculative, it was obviously considered one of the better bets by the experts.

Go with the consensus of experts, not with your favorite theory or your favorite expert. This rule applies to studies in general, but there are additional criteria we can use to judge the reliability and import of research. In diet and medicine, experimental results are often affected by a multitude of factors that are difficult to control for while remaining within ethics rules. People react differently to food and medicines, and a diet that works for one individual may not work for another. For health studies, the first thing to look at is whether the experiment involved living humans. Many experiments on food and drugs are performed in cell cultures (*in vitro*) or in animals. Showing that a compound is effective against disease when it enters cells is an excellent first step in testing a potential therapy.

However, such studies tell us little about side effects, and there is often no easy way to get the compound to the diseased cells in a living human body.

For example, you may have read that turmeric is a potent antioxidant in *in vitro* studies. Antioxidants reduce stress in cells and are thought to ward off cancers, inflammation, and even aging. Consequently, many people have added turmeric to their diets. Of course, purveyors of turmeric are happy to tell you about the *in vitro* antioxidant effects of the spice. The problem is that the vast majority of what we eat is broken down by our digestive system long before it has any chance of making it to our cells. Indeed, this is a feature and not a bug in our digestive system. Thus far, turmeric has failed to show any anti-inflammatory benefit in studies of humans.[34]

If a health study is only in animals or test tubes, the research is in its early stages. It is generally irrational to change your diet or take supplements based on such early-stage research.

Assuming a study does look at humans, the next thing to consider is the number of experimental subjects who participated in the study. If the number of subjects is less than 50, the results are not sufficiently meaningful to change your daily

---

[34] Nelson, K. M., Dahlin, J. L., Bisson, J., Graham, J., Pauli, G. F., & Walters, M. A. (2017). *The Essential Medicinal Chemistry of Curcumin.* Journal of medicinal chemistry, 60(5), 1620–1637. https://doi.org/10.1021/acs.jmedchem.6b00975.

routine. If the number of participants is more than 500, the results are more likely to be significant. The smaller the number of participants, the more likely it is that chance led to any surprising results. If the number of participants in a study is small, surprising conclusions are relatively unlikely to hold up in larger studies.

How were subjects conscripted into the study? Anything less than randomly selecting large numbers of people is going to introduce some sort of bias. One excellent example of this is in opinion polling. You might think that random phone surveys would be a good way to gauge public opinion. However, Pew Research reported in 2019 that only about 6% of people now participate in such polls, compared to 36% in 1997.[35] This suggests that participants in these surveys are no longer a representative cross-section of Americans. If you participate in phone polls, you are unusual.

Concerning in recent years is the subjects of psychological studies at U.S. universities. Most university psychology studies recruit subjects from Western, educated, industrialized, rich, and democratic states (WEIRD). As a result, the universality of psychological research has been called into question.

---

[35] Courtney Kennedy and Hannah Hartig (Feb 27 2019). *Response rates in telephone surveys have resumed their decline.* Pew Research, https://www.pewresearch.org/fact-tank/2019/02/27/response-rates-in-telephone-surveys-have-resumed-their-decline.

Randomized recruitment is just the first step in any great study. The next step is randomly assigning recruits into intervention and control groups. In retrospective studies, this is usually not possible. For example, during the COVID-19 pandemic, hospitals treated patients as best they could. In most cases, this means physicians chose therapies based on their knowledge of patient needs and the availability of therapeutics. If we comb through the medical records and look at how patients fared based on the treatments they received, we have not randomized the treatment and nontreatment groups because the choice of therapy for each patient was not made at random. It may be that only the sickest patients received a particular therapy, so if more patients died on that therapy, it may not have been the therapy that killed them but the seriousness of their condition beforehand.

In other cases, it may not be ethical to withhold a treatment from a patient at random, so some randomized trials cannot be performed for ethical reasons. Yet, if we really want to know whether a therapy is effective, we typically need some sort of randomization. If a study randomly selected subjects into intervention and control groups, the study conclusion is more compelling than if the study was merely observational.

We previously discussed the placebo effect. Knowing that one is being treated can have a profound effect on one's pain, stress, and sense of well-being. To isolate this psychosomatic effect from the effect of the therapy itself, researchers use a technique called blinding. The idea is to treat the control group exactly like the intervention group. If both groups receive consultations and pills that look the same, any differences between the groups are due to what is in the pill, not merely because the patients felt cared for. The best studies use double-blinding—even the people administering the treatments do not know which treatments are real therapy versus placebo. The gold standard of scientific research is the randomized controlled trial. The trial is double-blind where applicable, and subjects are sorted at random into control and intervention groups.

If a study is large, randomized, and double-blind, its conclusions are likely to be reliable.

5.9   Rational Judgment Questionnaire

When you encounter a news story quoting studies or alleging a conspiracy, ask yourself the following questions. Answering some of these questions may require further research.

What is my intuitive reaction?	If you have a strong emotional reaction to the news story, make a note of your reaction. You will need to apply countermeasures to prevent yourself from cherry-picking research favorable to your cause.
Does my ideological position truly depend on these alleged facts?	If the facts seem aligned with or opposed to your ideology or values, ask yourself whether your ideological position depends on these facts. When you realize that the facts are not as hostile as they first appear, you will have an easier time accepting them if they are true.
What facts would alter my ideological position?	If the alleged facts are insufficient to alter your ideological position, try to imagine hypothetical facts that would be strong enough to alter your point of view.

Is there a consensus of experts?	You may need to do some research to figure out if the experts in the field agree with the facts being presented. If the experts do not agree, you can discount the conclusions in the article.
Are you reading about an anomaly with respect to an established theory?	Anomalies are to be expected from errors in reporting, coincidences, and special circumstances. Isolated anomalies are not enough to displace a well-established theory. If the scientific consensus is not concerned, you should not be concerned either.
Does the author or source express that expert consensus?	Sometimes, an author misrepresents the consensus. This is a fact worth checking.
If the story is original reporting, is the source a reliable media outlet?	If the reporter does not work for an organization that requires anonymous sources to be checked, the original reporting is suspect. If the story is real, it will be confirmed by elite media sources.
If it is an "expert opinion," is the expert a pundit or predictor?	Is the expert required to make frequent, accurate predictions to keep their job? If not, their predictions and policy recommendations may be no better than guesses.

Am I an expert relative to experts?	An author may appear expert because they are saying many things you already believe to be true. However, your own expertise may be overestimated. Compare your expertise to that of the best experts, not to that of your peers.
Is the evidence accumulating, or are studies equivocal?	If studies cannot agree on a conclusion, the reported effect is probably vanishingly small or nonexistent. Wait until the results of studies agree.
Are there accusations of mass conspiracy?	If the author alleges a mass conspiracy among scientists, the author does not like the scientific consensus and is probably selling pseudoscience. The only organizations that can pull off mass conspiracies are industry trade groups and intelligence agencies.
Are you looking at a health or dietary study?	If the experiment alleges positive effects of a drug or compound, but tests are on animals or cells in a lab, the product may have little effect on humans via ingestion.
How many humans were studied in the experiment?	If the number of subjects is under 150, the results may not be reproducible because the chances of statistical error are relatively high.

How were human subjects selected for the experiment or poll?	Almost every method of selecting subjects for an experiment carries a bias. For example, the subjects may have been wealthier than average or may have joined the study because they had a medical complaint.
Was the study randomized, or observational?	An observational study can be affected by many factors because people choose their foods and treatments based on multiple lifestyle factors. A randomized study is more likely to average out any irrelevant factors.
Was the experiment blinded with a placebo?	When subjects know they are receiving a treatment, the mere knowledge that they are being treated may alter their perceptions, stress levels, expectations, or lifestyle in subtle ways.
Was the study double-blind, or did the researchers know who was receiving the placebo?	Those administering an experiment are vulnerable to subconscious biases, and they may treat subjects differently if they know who is receiving the placebo.

6 CONCLUSION

6.1   The End of the Beginning

This book is a primer on rationality. To keep this work short and accessible, I have simplified the topic as much as possible. Some will say I have oversimplified it.

We have walked through the conceptual foundations of rationality and begun to understand Bayesian reasoning, the ideal of rational inference. We have also examined some of the ways that our cognitive biases will predictably throw us off course—unless we take care to overcome our biases. I hope that this picture, streamlined though it may be, helps you put the task of reasoning in better perspective.

Please consider this treatment the beginning of your rationality education. There is much more to learn about almost every aspect of rationality than I have written here. There are entire books describing human cognitive biases and the fascinating experiments that expose them. There are philosophical questions about whether Bayesian reasoning is the complete answer or whether it has limitations. Rationality is a relatively young field, and there is plenty of new research being done. Researchers are still studying how to teach rational thinking ability and whether biases vary across cultures.

I can barely imagine trying to think for myself without the benefit of basic rationality mindware, yet almost no schools teach the subject except within narrow specialties. I hope that this short introduction has made you feel the same way.

6.2   Imagining a Rational Future

The scientific revolution gave civilization a new vocabulary and a new way of looking at the world. The revolution gave the world the scientific method, science education, the professional scientist, and a scientific approach to almost anything that can be measured. What would a rational revolution look like, and how might it change society?

Humanity's knowledge of rational principles and cognitive bias is much like any other aspect of human knowledge. Eventually, it will find greater utility in business, medicine, science, and the humanities. In narrow disciplines, rational principles are already part of the mainstream. Artificial intelligence, deep learning, search and rescue, and business management all make use of Bayesian analysis and cognitive bias, even if they do not connect it with rationality in general. The methods of rationality are slowly finding application in society, but

Conclusion

its current trajectory leaves most of it siloed within narrow domains and within the boundaries of business marketing and military intelligence organizations.

A true rational revolution will be more democratic. Everyone should be inoculated against marketing designed to exploit our biases. It makes no sense that corporations and intelligence agencies routinely use rationality know-how, while the average citizen remains in the dark. Everyone should be able to see through sales marketing ploys or fake news from special interests. We should all be able to read the news and understand what is going on in the world.

To achieve this democratic goal, we must teach rationality in the classroom. A high school course on rationality could easily fill one semester, or about 120 hours of classwork. In corporate and continuing education settings, a week of full-time training would be enough to cover the basics, while semiannual, one-day refreshers would keep busy professionals aligned with a culture that overcomes bias and promotes reason.

I am passionate about truth for truth's sake, but there are also economic and national security advantages to having a rational workforce and a rational electorate. MBA programs teach students about cognitive biases because they are relevant to business management. Imagine if your entire workforce had key elements of MBA training. Surely, public policy ought to improve when voters learn how to filter out fake news and leverage true expertise.

Rationality could become an important sector of the economy. Educational services are just one opportunity for trained rationality experts. With rationality

209

training, we would become more aware of our limitations and better use our human capabilities. Yet, human capacities are likely to be augmented with software. Augmented rationality may take the form of web browser plug-ins, or it might operate in the cloud as part of your social media platforms.

In the sciences, researchers spend much of their time evaluating the work of other investigators. Scientists want to know what inferences have already been made and how strong those inferences are. Perhaps rationality engineers will develop tools and techniques for evaluating the entire web of human knowledge. By encoding all human expertise into a Bayesian network, engineers could answer questions such as:

- Where are our weakest links in our knowledge of the human immune system?
- What experiments are most likely to have the most impact?
- In what areas of knowledge are we most confident, and how can we leverage that confidence in to explore new areas of knowledge?
- As a non-expert, precisely how did climate scientists reach consensus on anthropogenic climate change?

In the last chapter, we looked at the importance of evaluating expertise and following the consensus of experts. Today, this is a nontrivial task, but perhaps there are rationalist opportunities to make the task more straightforward. Are there ways to map the depth and breadth of an individual's expertise more accurately and systematically? Are there better ways to assess the consensus of experts than reliance on press reports?

Change will be not only technical and institutional but cultural. Freedom of speech and thought are precious, and they cannot be legislated away. At the same time, we must acknowledge that many of the opinions people feel entitled to are not really opinions at all but instead commitments to falsehoods. One cannot have the "opinion" that the Earth is flat or that vaccines cause autism when there is well-established fact (i.e., inference and expert consensus) to the contrary. Similarly, one cannot maintain a rational conviction that a proposition is true when the expert consensus is that we do not yet know. The law protects our right to say and believe anything at all, but our culture should not welcome such an assault on rationality. We should accord our confidence with the consensus of experts, not with our fantasies or with those who will tell us what we desire to hear.

On the opposite end of the spectrum, we should regard our fetish for absolute certainty as equally irrational. Knowledge comes in degrees, and we do not require certainty to feel secure in knowledge. We merely need to be confident enough for the task at hand.

Modern culture remains surprisingly tribal and egoistic. Kathryn Schulz, a self-described "wrongologist," has written a book entitled *Being Wrong*.[36] Coming to terms with being wrong about things is a key rational skill. Admitting and correcting our errors also has the potential to bring out the best in us. As Schulz writes:

> *This is one of the most powerful ways being wrong can transform us: it can help us become more compassionate people. Being right might be fun but, as we've seen, it has a tendency to bring out the worst in us. By contrast, being wrong is often the farthest thing in the world from fun—and yet, in the end, it has the potential to bring out the best in us.*

The cultural changes I describe here are truly massive. Yet, other cultural shifts in Western society over the last 30 years have also been profound. Contemporary culture is more compassionate and reflective in its discourse about people of differing abilities, ethnic background, and sexual orientation. If we can drastically change the way we talk about ethnicity and sexual orientation in 30 years, why not alter our discourse about rationality in the next decade?

Of course, in forecasting the future, I am engaging in speculation. We do not yet know the full extent to which we can modify cultural norms. Nor do we know how

---

[36] Kathryn Schulz (2010). *Being Wrong: Adventures in the Margin of Error*. Ecco. ISBN 0061176044.

technology can most effectively augment human rationality. However, I am confident that understanding rational methods and cognitive biases will be key to meeting these challenges.

If you are looking to make a positive change in the world, the opportunity is before you. I hope you find this book inspiring.

RESOURCES

The Rational Future Institute

The goal of the Rational Future Institute is to promote cultural awareness of the principles of ideal rationality and of the ways we humans predictably deviate from rational thinking. To that end, the Rational Future Institute develops lesson plans and educational materials on rational thinking.

https://rationalfuture.org

LessWrong

LessWrong is a community blog dedicated to improving reasoning and decision making. The site was founded in 2009 by Eliezer Yudkowsky, an AI researcher who has been pivotal in popularizing topics in rationality. Yudkowsky was the first to introduce me to Bayesian reasoning.

On LessWrong, you will find posts by community members on epistemic and instrumental rationality, decision making, AI, philosophy, and self-help.

https://lesswrong.com

Steven Pinker

In 2020, cognitive scientist Steven Pinker taught a course on rationality at Harvard University, and the lectures are available for free online. Pinker has also announced a forthcoming book on rationality.

https://stevenpinker.com/classes/rationality-gened-1066

Clearer Thinking

Clearer Thinking takes recent insights into cognition and psychology and develops tools and mini-courses that aim to help you understand yourself and the world around you, improve your mood, and make better decisions. As of January 2021, there were 50 tools and courses on the menu.

https://clearerthinking.org

Center For Applied Rationality (CFAR)

I advocate for bringing the basic concepts of rationality to the masses as a tool to enhance critical thinking. At present, CFAR employs a different strategy for creating a more rational world—CFAR is "finding and developing high-promise individuals," delivering intense workshops in applied rationality, and studying the effects of the training on their alumni. What I love about the CFAR approach is that they study the effects of specific rationality training techniques to discover which lessons truly have a positive effect in practice.

The Foundation for Critical Thinking

The Foundation promotes critical thinking in schools and culture more generally. They maintain a library of publications, teach courses and workshops, and organize critical thinking conferences. Though the Foundation does not emphasize ideal rationality, they have a wealth of resources for teaching traditional critical thinking.

https://criticalthinking.org

INDEX

D

E

G

H

I

Index

Printed in the USA
CPSIA information can be obtained
at www.ICGtesting.com
LVHW041726170124
769199LV00002B/9

9 781736 578339